CARGO N🖊TES

2nd Edition

Dhananjay Swadi

Witherby Seamanship International
A Division of Witherby Publishing Group Ltd

4 Dunlop Square, Livingston, Edinburgh, EH54 8SB, Scotland, UK

Tel No: +44(0)1506 463 227 - Fax No: +44(0)1506 468 999
Email: info@emailws.com - Web: www.witherbyseamanship.com

First published 2005
2nd Edition 2009
Reprinted 2010

ISBN 1-905331-61-1

© Witherby Publishing Group Ltd, 2010

British Library Cataloguing in Publication Data
A catalogue record for this book is available from the British Library.

Printed and bound in Great Britain by Bell & Bain Ltd, Glasgow

Published by
Witherby Publishing Group Ltd
4 Dunlop Square, Livingston,
Edinburgh, EH54 8SB,
Scotland, UK

Tel No: +44(0)1506 463 227
Fax No: +44(0)1506 468 999

Email: info@emailws.com
Web: www.witherbys.com

Dhananjay Swadi

Dhananjay Swadi has over 12 years' experience at sea on a wide variety of ships, including container ships, gas tankers and bulk carriers, culminating as a Chief Officer with Maersk. In addition to his Master's certificate, Mr Swadi also has a master's degree in Marine Policy with a distinction from Cardiff University. Until recently, Mr Swadi was a lecturer at the Glasgow College of Nautical Studies teaching a wide variety of subjects including Cargowork, Marine Law and Maritime Economics. In January 2006, he joined Northern Marine Management as Manning Manager.

FOREWORD

'Cargo Notes', by Dhananjay Swadi, gathers together in one place a wealth of factual information that is taken from a variety of well respected and recognised sources, including official publications, concerned with the carriage and handling of cargoes. The information is presented in a logical and clear format comprising two well-indexed sections, the first on Dry Cargoes and the second on Liquid and Gas. Within each section, the basic concepts behind safe carriage are first considered, and then progressively developed, to show the modern methods utilised in today's Shipping Industry.

Cargo Notes is ideally suited to seafarers preparing to sit written or oral examinations leading to Deck Officer Certificates of Competency. It is also a relevant reference work for onboard usage and as a guide for cargo watchkeeping Officers. It is an ideal companion to sister publications from Seamanship International (now Witherby Seamanship) on Seamanship and Ship Stability and is a worthwhile addition to any nautical library.

Richard Speight MSc FNI

Depute and Assistant Principal
Glasgow College of Nautical Studies
September 2005

CONTENTS

Dry Cargoes

1

KEY POINTS

♦ A cargo plan provides information about the cargo and its location onboard the vessel

♦ an updated cargo plan must be available for reference in case of an emergency

♦ cargo plans differ from trade to trade and, in certain cases, may need to be submitted in advance by the vessel to the port or terminal

♦ the shipper must provide sufficient cargo related information in advance of loading for the vessel to prepare a viable cargo plan.

Information that is contained on a typical cargo plan:

- Name of the vessel
- voyage number
- loading port(s)
- discharging port(s)
- draughts for'd and aft
- name of the Master
- schematic of the vessel showing:
  - Location of cargo for different ports
  - Cargo quantities
  - Location of any dangerous or special cargo.

Information that is required from the shipper[1]:

1. *In the case of general cargo and cargo carried in cargo units, a general description of the cargo, the gross mass of the cargo or cargo units and any relevant special properties of the cargo.*

2. *In the case of bulk cargoes, information on the stowage factor of the cargo, the trimming procedures, the likelihood of shifting, including angle of repose if applicable, and any other relevant special properties. In the case of a concentrate or other cargo which may liquefy, additional information in the form of a certificate indicating the moisture content of the cargo and its transportable moisture limit.*

3. *In the case of bulk cargoes, information on any chemical properties that may create a potential hazard.*

Using the information provided by the Shipper, the Master should ensure that:

1. The different commodities to be carried are compatible with each other or suitably separated.

2. The cargo is suitable for the ship.

3. The ship is suitable for the cargo.

4. The cargo can be safely stowed and secured onboard the ship and transported under all expected conditions during the intended voyage.

[1] *Extracted from SI 336; The Merchant Shipping (Carriage of Cargoes) Regulations 1999*

When the cargo consignment is delivered to the terminal, a dock receipt is issued to the person delivering it. This contains all relevant information about the cargo, such as the weight, volume, number of pieces etc.

If any damage to the cargo is noticed at this delivery stage, the dock receipt is so endorsed. This document is used to calculate the freight and other handling costs.

When the cargo is transferred to the carrying vessel, the terminal issues a *Mates Receipt*, which is then signed by the vessel. At this stage, it is important to carefully note any damage to the cargo and endorse the Mates Receipt accordingly. A Mates Receipt should only be signed once it has been verified that the goods are actually loaded on board. On general cargo vessels, this is usually done by comparing with the *tally sheets* made up by a *tally clerk*. In the container trade, it is usually carried out by the shore agency of the carrier, who signs the Mates Receipts on behalf of the vessel's command.

The Mates Receipt is used to compile the *Bill of Lading (B/L)*. A B/L is the primary document that governs commercial transactions at sea. It performs three main functions:

• It is a *receipt* for the goods carried

• it is *evidence* of the contract of carriage

• it is a *Document of Title*. This means that the holder of a B/L, in good faith, is entitled to the delivery of the cargo.

The B/L is generally endorsed according to the Mates Receipts. In many cases, shippers require a clean B/L because of the requirements of their letters of credit, and may offer a *letter of indemnity* against a clean (unendorsed) B/L. The letter of indemnity has been proven to be of little value against a cargo claim. The best way to ensure a clean B/L is to ship undamaged cargo. However, letters of indemnity are used in some trades, including tankers, but should not be accepted unless approved by the company and P&I club.

B/Ls can be of a number of different types. The main types in common use are:

Negotiable B/L

A document of title that can be transferred between persons or companies by endorsing in the proper place. The person that presents a suitably endorsed B/L at the discharge port gains possession of the cargo.

Non-Negotiable (Straight) B/L

This type of a B/L cannot be transferred and only the named person, or his representative, can gain possession of the cargo at the discharge port.

Combined Transport B/L

In the container trade, where one carrier often takes responsibility for the door-to-door transport of the cargo, this is a common type of B/L.

Through B/L

This is issued by the sea-carrier but states that he is responsible for the goods only during the sea passage part of the total transit.

Seaway bill

This takes the same form as a B/L but is a non-negotiable receipt and not a document of title. This is usual in the container trade and is only a receipt for the goods carried and evidence of a contract between the shipper and the carrier. It does not need to be presented for delivery of the cargo.

A B/L has to be stamped and signed by the Master. In the container trade, due to the difficulty of presenting the B/L to the Master in time for the vessel to sail, the Master issues a letter, or power of attorney, to the carrier's agents, authorising the agent to sign the B/Ls on his behalf.

The document used for customs clearance in the destination country is the *Cargo Manifest*. This is a comprehensive list of all cargo for that destination and is made up from information contained within the B/Ls.

A *Dangerous Goods Declaration* must be provided to the Master by the shipper of any goods that come under the auspices of the IMDG Code[1].

A *Dangerous Goods Manifest* is compiled from bookings and provided to the vessel before loading commences. If necessary, it is revised before sailing. This document lists the weight, quantity, packaging, class and stowage of all hazardous cargo on the vessel. It is compiled by the agent and signed by the master and agent.

[1] *See the section on the IMDG Code for further information.*

SIAM
INTERNATIONAL FREIGHTLINES

OCEAN BILL OF LADING

SHIPPER/EXPORTER			
MR. VORAVIT KOSOL 1100 S.W. CLAY STREET PORTLAND, OR 97201 U.S.A.			

BOOKING NO.
LAXBGK D 03628

EXPORT REFERENCES
04380/BKK

CONSIGNEE
MR. VORAVIT KOSOL
18/1 COVENT ROAD
SILOM, BANGKOK THAILAND

FORWARDING AGENT FMC NO
SIAM INTERNATIONAL FREIGHLINE
OTI NO. 12475NF

POINT AND COUNTRY OF ORIGIN OF GOODS
PORTLAND

NOTIFY PARTY
SAME AS ABOVE'
635 3443

ALSO NOTIFY – ROUTING AND INSTRUCTIONS
TRIUMPH INTERFREIGHT
537/197 SATHUPRADIT COMPLEX
YANNAWA BANGKOK THAILAND
TEL: 2942095

* INITIAL CARRIAGE BY	* PLACE OF INITIAL RECEIPT PORTLAND
EXPORTING CARRIER APL ENGLAND V 103	PORT OF LOADING LONG BEACH

LOADING PIER TERMINAL

AIR/SEA PORT OF DISCHARGE BANGKOK THAILAND	* PLACE OF DELIVERY BY ON CARRIER

TYPE OF MOVE

PARTICULARS FURNISHED BY SHIPPER

MARKS AND NUMBERS	NO. OF PKGS.	HM	DESCRIPTION OF PACKAGES AND GOODS	GROSS WEIGHT	MEASUREMENTS
VORAVIT KOSOL BANGKOK THAILAND	61 BOXES (3SKIDS)		SAID TO CONTAIN: 61 CARTONS OF USED HOUSEHOLD AND PERSONAL EFFECTS FREIGHT PREPAID SKID DIMENSION: 53 x 40 x 69 INCHES (LxWxR) 48 x 42 x 52 INCHES 50 x 48 x 59 INCHES	2680LBS CLEAN ONBOARD V/V APL ENGLAND V103 DATED: JUL15,2001	227.25CUF V.435CBM

SHIPPERS DECLARED VALUE $ _____ SUBJECT TO EXTRA FREIGHT
AS PER TARIFF AND CARRIERS LIMITS REFER TO CLAUSE 18 HEREOF

FREIGHT PAYABLE AT BY

FREIGHT CHARGES	PREPAID	COLLECT	
227.25 CUF X 4.00 PER CUF	$ 909.00		Received the goods, or packages said to contain goods herein mentioned, in apparent good order and condition unless otherwise indicated, to be transported and delivered, to trans-shipped as herein provided. The carriage is subject to the provisions of the U.S. Carriage of Goods by Sea Act of 1936. All the terms and conditions of the Carrier's regular form Bill of Lading, as filed with the Federal Maritime Commission available to any shipper or consignee upon request, are incorporated with the force and effect as if they were written at length herein, and all such terms and conditions so incorporated by reference are agreed by Shipper to be binding and to govern the relations, whatever they may be between those included in the words "Shipper" and "Carrier" as defined in Carriers regular form Bill of Lading. IN WITNESS WHEREOF, the Carrier has signed and the Shipper has received THREE (3) original bills of lading. ONE of which being accomplished, the others to stand void.
			SIAM INTERNATIONAL FREIGHTLINES
TOTAL CHARGES			Dated At _____ By NANCY S. AS CARRIER MO JUL DAY 15 YEAR 2001
* APPLICABLE ONLY WHEN DOCUMENT USED AS A THROUGH BILL OF LADING			**BL. No.** 04380/BKK

Example of a Bill of Lading

Cargo Responsibilities

The cargo officers are responsible for the safe and efficient handling and stowage of cargo, for the correct preparation of cargo spaces and for the correct supervision of its loading. The officers should liaise with other ship staff and key members of shore staff, ie foremen, tally clerks, terminal operators, etc.

Checks to be made prior to the cargo being loaded

1. Check that holds are clean, dry and ready to receive the cargo. If any dunnage is laid, it should be inspected.

2. Hold inspection should include the inspection of plating, access ladders, lighting, guard rails, storm valves and pipes, fire fighting gear and fittings, manhole covers, spar ceiling, etc.

3. Check that all lifting plant (derricks, cranes, wires, blocks, etc) are in good order and properly rigged. Check all cargo gear is certificated and tested. Ensure that a proper risk assessment is in place prior to using the lifting gear.

4. All lashing gear must be in place and inspected, as is described in Section 1.13.

Checks to be made during loading to ensure that the cargo is not damaged

1. Check acceptability of the cargo. The cargo must be dry and in apparent good condition. Check for damage. If the cargo is sensitive to moisture, ensure proper conditions throughout loading are maintained. Close hatches during rain where necessary.

2. Visually check the cargo while it is being loaded. Inspect the cargo for damage. Cargo may have been subject to damage while in transit to the dock, on the quayside or during loading. Damage to cargo may be caused by incorrect stowage or slinging, careless use of mechanical handling equipment, eg forklift trucks, insufficient attention to labelling and marking, carelessly packed units, insufficient dunnaging or packaging, incorrect ventilation settings or, in the case of refrigerated cargo, incorrect set points.

3. Check correct handling and use of cargo handling equipment. For example, cargo hooks should never be used when discharging fragile cargo.

4. The Cargo Officer must be familiar with the ship's specialised cargo gear.

5. Check cargo sling arrangements to safeguard against the cargo being dropped or incorrect Safe Working Load (SWL) slings being used.

6. The stowage of all cargo should be checked with reference to the cargo plan. Particular attention should be paid to the loading of dangerous or refrigerated cargo. Reefers must be plugged in immediately and the temperature noted.

7. When stowing general cargo, preventative measures should be taken to ensure against the possibility of fragile goods being crushed when stowed with heavy goods.

8. Some cargoes are liable to damage from taint. These should not be stowed next to strong smelling cargoes.

Procedure for dealing with damaged cargo

If any discrepancies with the condition of the cargo appear, a Cargo Damage or Exception Form should be filled out and given to the stevedores prior to the ship sailing. The Master should report any discrepancies associated with the quantity of cargo loaded or discharged on a letter of protest.

The Cargo Damage Report is a statement of damage to the cargo that gives all of the details. Damage reports should have certain essential items recorded on them, eg cargo marks, commodity type, container type and number involved, stowage location, when discovered, extent of damage and the time of the discovery. It may be necessary to get the damage surveyed prior to loading or even to reject the cargo in serious cases. Both the Mates Receipt and B/L should be enclosed appropriately.

Checks after completion of cargo

1. All cargo securing arrangements and lashings should be checked. Check all lashing gear is in good order. Check bottom tiers of containers are secure and that twist locks are in position and locked before subsequent tiers are loaded.

2. When cargo operations are finished for the day, hatches should be closed and secured for sea.

3. The amount of cargo worked that day should be recorded and the draughts fore, aft and amidships taken and recorded in the Deck Logbook.

4. Throughout the cargo watch, a notebook should be carried and a note of all relevant occurrences made, eg times when heavy lifts loaded, times when work commences and ceases at each of the hatches, number of gangs onboard, times when deck lashings checked, completion times for hatches, etc. These notes will then be transferred to the Deck Logbook and will be compared with the shore tally sheet.

Besides the items above, the watchkeeping officer is responsible for a whole range of activities including monitoring safety, pollution prevention and other matters related with watchkeeping in port.

Relevant extracts from STCW'95, Chapter 8 *Watchkeeping in Port*, are included in the appendix and should be referred to in addition to the above.

Preparing a hold after a cargo of coal

A charter party or contract of carriage normally requires the owner to "... *make the holds, refrigerating and cooling chambers and all other parts of the ship where goods are carried, fit and safe for their reception, carriage and preservation*".

The owner is also required to present the holds 'clean and dry' prior to commencement of loading. If the owner fails to present his ship in a fit state to receive the cargo, he risks cargo

contamination claims amounting to large sums of money. It is, therefore, of the utmost importance that the owner makes all efforts to prepare the cargo holds of his ship prior to loading.

The preparation of the holds that is carried out for the next cargo depends on a number of factors:

• The last cargo carried

• the requirements of the next cargo

• the time available

• the equipment and manpower available.

If the next cargo is compatible with the last, a good sweep down and removal of leftover cargo is all that is required. If, however, the next cargo is incompatible with the last or if you are loading sensitive cargoes such as foodstuffs, a more thorough cleaning may be required.

The following is a hold cleaning sequence that is generally followed on bulk carriers after all enclosed space procedures have been followed:

1. Remove all residues of the previous cargo. Sweeping down and collecting cargo residues for removal usually achieves this.

2. Any dunnage that is left over in the holds is stacked and removed.

3. Holds are then usually washed with seawater and, if required, with a final rinse of fresh water. A fresh water rinse can reduce corrosion and accelerate drying. Special attention needs to be given to remove residues from areas that can be difficult to reach, such as hatch covers and frames.

4. Bilges and strum boxes are to be properly cleaned and, if necessary, the bilge area is to be disinfected or lime washed. Bilges are then covered with burlap to prevent entry of cargo particles.

5. Hold inspection to be carried out and any damages repaired.

6. Ancillary systems, such as the fixed fire fighting equipment or ventilation equipment, must be tested.

7. New dunnage should be laid out if required.

8. Hold lighting to be checked.

9. Means of access should be checked for damage and must be free of any hazards.

10. Cargo gear must be checked and rigged for loading or discharge.

11. Hatch covers must be examined for weathertight integrity and, if necessary, the rubber packing renewed.

12. Fumigation is to be carried out if the charterers or cargo owners require it. The IMO publication *'Recommendations on the safe use of pesticides at sea' and MGN 284 'Recommendation for ships carrying fumigated bulk cargoes'* must be referred to.

13. Air pipes, fixtures and fittings must be checked and any repairs carried out.

Wood Dunnage

The word 'dunnage' is an old sailing term for material placed between cargoes to prevent shifting.

Uses of dunnage:

- *To provide protection to the cargo from water damage caused by contact with water from the bilges, other cargo or double bottom tanks*

- *it protects moisture-sensitive cargoes, such as bagged cargo (eg coffee, cocoa) or bales (eg tobacco, tea) from sweat, which forms on a ship's sides and runs off over the decks*

- *to provide air channels between stows to aid ventilation, mainly for refrigerated cargoes*

- *to prevent damage to goods through contact with either the ship's structure or with other cargo*

- *to aid in the effective distribution of weight on tank tops or hatch covers*

- *to aid in filling void spaces between cargoes, especially unevenly shaped cargoes.*

Dunnage may be divided into floor, lateral, interlayer and top dunnage.

Floor dunnage
This is mainly used in general cargo ships, to lift the cargo off the tank top. This prevents cargo damage from sweat or moisture running off from other cargo. Floor dunnage is laid crosswise and the direction depends on the design of the vessel. In ships with lateral water drainage (bilges), the first layer must be laid cross wise, while in ships with fore and aft water drainage (wells), the first layer must be laid lengthwise. The dunnage should be laid close together to prevent the cargo from making contact with the tank top. On modern vessels, especially reefers, permanent deck gratings, made of grooved and perforated aluminium or plywood gratings, are fitted.

Lateral dunnage
This usually takes the shape of a *spar ceiling* on a general cargo vessel. These are wooden beams securely connected to the side of the cargo hold. Lateral dunnage prevents contact of the cargo with the ship's side and so prevents cargo damage due to sweat. In the absence of spar ceilings,

Wooden Dunnage Secured to Hold Side[1]

wooden or crisscross dunnage must be used. Crisscross dunnage consists of nailed grids, cross-wise wooden dunnage being nailed to vertical uprights (vertically positioned squared beams).

Permanent Collapsible Dunnage (PCDs)

This comprises of painted or varnished 8' × 4' plywood sheets that may be fitted to the ship's sides. These sheets are hinged at their base and open out to be secured in a variety of ways. Their main purpose is to 'square off' curved ship sides and they are particularly useful for palletised cargo.

Interlayer dunnage

This separates cargoes from each other, either for the protection of an underlying cargo from contamination by a top cargo or for the segregation of individual batches of cargo.

Top dunnage

This generally protects the cargo from contamination damage from water, hydraulic oil, etc dripping from the weather decks. Top dunnage must also allow for some air circulation and evaporation, especially for hygroscopic cargoes. For this reason, top dunnage is usually made from an air permeable material such as paper or jute.

Any wooden dunnage used must be dry to prevent moisture damage. The *'Transport Information Service (TIS[2])'* from the German Insurance Association recommends a water content of no more than 12-15%, air dried. Any wooden dunnage that is too fresh or has been exposed to the atmosphere must not be used.

On modern reefer vessels, increasing use is being made of inflatable dunnage. This has the advantage of being re-usable. It is inflated using compressed air, which is readily available on board.

Dunnage is also used within freight containers to prevent sweat damage. As standard containers cannot be easily ventilated, humidity levels inside can rise and significant amounts of moisture can condense on the sides and the bottom. To prevent damage to the cargo, top, side and bottom dunnage is used. This can be moisture absorbent paper, timber to chock and secure the cargo on the sides, or plastic tarpaulins. The tarpaulins are suspended under the container ceiling (not in contact with the cargo if at all possible) and have 'reservoirs' in which the sweat may collect as it drips.

Reprinted from Cargo Work by DJ House, published by 'Elsevier'
http://www.tis-gdv.de/- cargo information – dunnage

KEY POINTS

♦ **It is often necessary to separate different parcels of the same cargo**

♦ **methods of separation differ from trade to trade**

♦ **break-bulk cargo is often stencilled with individual identifying marks.**

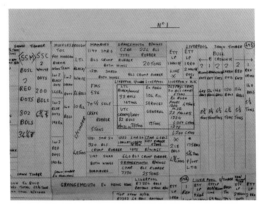

Handwritten Cargo Plan

Types of Separation

On general cargo ships, parcels of the same cargo for discharge to different ports are often separated. Some of the more common means of separation include:

- Coloured polythene sheets

- burlap, which is often used as a separation for bagged cargoes in the break-bulk trade

- tarpaulin, which can be used to separate cargoes such as bulk grain particularly on handy sized bulk carriers

- cargo nets. Polypropylene mesh nets can be used to separate cargo parcels in the same hold

- paint. Timber can be separated by paint, usually water based. Steel rails and coils can be separated by paint or coloured tape

- marking tape. On Ro Ro vessels, cars of the same type for discharge at different ports are often separated using either 'hazard' tape or coloured marking tape.

Marking of cargo

To prevent over carriage[1], and to allow freight forwarders to correctly identify cargoes, most break bulk cargoes are labelled or stencilled with identifying marks. These marks can form a part of the B/L description of the cargo (see Section 1.2).

[1] Inadvertent carriage of cargoes to the next port

KEY POINTS

♦ **Moisture damage can be a source of significant cargo claims**

♦ **most claims are as a result of a failure to correctly ventilate the cargo hold, causing cargo sweat or ship sweat.**

Ships may be fitted with natural or forced ventilation systems. These may be used for:

• Prevention of cargo or ship sweat

• removal of taint or smell of previous cargoes

• prevention of the build-up of dangerous gases

• supply of fresh air to 'live' cargoes

• removal of the heat that is given off by certain cargoes.

When using the ventilation system to prevent ship or cargo sweat, continuous monitoring of the hold atmosphere must be carried out. This is because the moisture content of the cargo, coupled with variations in air temperature, cargo temperature and sea temperature, can dramatically influence the amounts of water vapour retained and released into the air inside a hold[1].

Types of cargoes affected

Hygroscopic cargoes
Hygroscopic products have natural moisture content and are mainly of plant origin. They may retain, absorb or release water vapour, and excessive amounts of inherent moisture may lead to significant self-heating and 'moisture migration' within the cargo. This can result in caking, mildew or rot. Examples of hygroscopic products include grain, rice, flour, sugar, cotton, tobacco, cocoa, coffee and tea.

Non-hygroscopic products
Non-hygroscopic products have no water content. However, certain commodities (eg steel) may be damaged if stowed in a moist environment. Others may be harmed if packaged using a hygroscopic material (eg wood, paper)

Types of Sweat

Cargo sweat
Cargo sweat refers to the condensation that may form on exposed surfaces of the cargo as a consequence of large amounts of warm, moist air being introduced into a hold containing substantially colder cargo. This usually occurs when the voyage is from a colder to a warmer place and the outside air has a *dewpoint*[2] above the temperature of the cargo. To prevent this sweat forming, all ventilation should be restricted until the temperature of the cargo is above the dewpoint temperature of the outside air.

[1] www.westpandi.com; loss prevention bulletin; February 2000
[2] When an isolated volume of air cools, relative humidity increases as the temperature falls. Once the temperature has descended to the level at which saturation occurs, water begins to condense. This temperature is known as the 'dewpoint'. This is generally measured by wet and dry bulb thermometers or by a 'whirling psychrometer'.

Ship's sweat

Ship's sweat refers to condensation that forms directly on a vessel's structure when the air within a hold, made warm and moist by the cargo, comes into contact with cold surfaces as the vessel moves into cooler climates. Cargo may be damaged by overhead drips, by contact with sweat that has formed on the ship's sides or by condensed water that may accumulate at the bottom of the hold. To prevent ship sweat, holds should be surface ventilated as long as the dewpoint of the outside air is lower than the temperature of the air inside.

If the dewpoint of both the outside and the hold air can be determined then the West of England P&I Club[3] advises the use of the 'Dewpoint Rule':

- VENTILATE if the dewpoint of the air inside the hold is higher than the dewpoint of the air outside the hold.
- DO NOT VENTILATE if the dewpoint of the air inside the hold is lower than the dewpoint of the air outside the hold.

The *three degrees rule* may be applied when it is impracticable to measure hold dewpoint temperatures accurately. In such cases, ventilation requirements may be estimated by, several times a day, comparing the average cargo temperature at the time of loading with the outside air temperature. Ventilation may then be carried out on the following basis:

- VENTILATE if the dry bulb temperature of the outside air is at least 3°C cooler than the average cargo temperature at the time of loading.
- DO NOT VENTILATE if the dry bulb temperature of the outside air is less than 3°C cooler than the average cargo temperature at the time of loading or warmer.

In order to apply the three degree rule, it will be necessary for the ship's staff to take a number of cargo temperature readings during loading.

In addition to ventilating the holds, hold inspections should be carried out whenever possible.

In general terms, hygroscopic cargoes need to be monitored more carefully than non-hygroscopic cargoes. Ventilation is rarely required if only non-hygroscopic cargoes are carried. As far as possible, hygroscopic and non-hygroscopic cargoes should not be stowed together because of the differing ventilation requirements.

Proper records and logs must be maintained to defend against cargo claims.

---

[3] www.westpandi.com; loss prevention bulletin; February 2000

1.8 Stowage Factor and Broken Stowage

Stowage Factor

This is the space occupied by a unit weight of cargo under normal conditions. A ship has a limited amount of space in which to load the cargo. The stowage factor of the cargo will allow calculation of the space it will occupy in the hold, given its weight. The lower the stowage factor, the denser the cargo. For example, iron ore has a stowage factor of 0.28 m³/t, while cotton waste has a stowage factor of 2.78 m³/t. The stowage factor of the same type of cargo may vary depending on the nature of cargo and the region from where it is sourced. Where bale goods are concerned, an important point is whether the bales are carried compressed or uncompressed. For example, hemp in bales uncompressed has a stowage factor of 7.3 m³/t, while the same cargo compressed has a stowage factor of 2.55 – 3.4 m³/t.

Relationship between Weight, Volume and Stowage Factor

Stowage factor is the volume occupied by a unit weight of cargo. Therefore, to convert a given weight to the corresponding volume, the following formula is used:

$$\text{Volume (m}^3) = \text{Weight (tons)} \times \text{Stowage Factor (SF) (m}^3/\text{t)}$$

Broken Stowage

This is the space lost through either the uneven nature of the cargo or the packaging or dunnage between cargoes.

It is often expressed as a percentage of the volume of the cargo and will vary with the nature of the cargo carried.

Calculation Examples

1. A 250 tonnes parcel of palletised cargo has an SF of 1.8 m³/t. Allowing for 5% broken stowage, calculate the space this parcel of cargo will occupy in a hold.

   $V = Wt \times SF$; $Wt = V/SF$;
   $SF = V/Wt$

   Volume Occupied 250×1.8
   $= 450$ m³

   5% Broken Stowage
   $= 5\% \times 450 = 22.5$ m³

   Space occupied $= 450 + 22.5$
   $= \textbf{472.5 m}^3$

   (Alternatively, $105\% \times 450$
   $= \textbf{472.5 m}^3$)

2. If the parcel is placed in a hold of 1200 m³ bale capacity, calculate the space remaining for other cargo.

   Space available $= 1200.0$ m³

   Space remaining $= 1200 - 472.5$
   $= \textbf{727.5 m}^3$

3. Calculate the weight of cargo, SF 1.3 m³/t BS 5%, that may be loaded in the remaining space.

The space remaining = 105% of the volume of cargo to load

$$727.5 \text{ m}^3 = 105\% \times \text{Volume of cargo}$$

$$\frac{727.5}{1.05} = \text{Volume of cargo to load}$$

Volume of cargo to load
= 692.86 m³

$$\text{Wt of cargo to load} = \frac{692.86 \text{ m}^3}{1.3 \text{ m}^3/\text{t}}$$

= 532.97 t

KEY POINTS

♦ **General cargo vessels tend to have their own gear to load and discharge cargoes**

♦ **cargo derricks come in a variety of designs and safe working loads.**

General Cargo Vessel

Many general cargo vessels have their own gear that helps them to load and discharge in ports lacking infrastructure. This is usually in the form of a derrick or crane serving each hold

and it is often a distinguishing feature of general cargo ships.

Single Swinging Derrick

The most basic form of cargo gear is the single derrick. This can be equipped with span tackles and cargo purchases.

The span blocks are secured to the mast of the derrick head and the 'topping wire' is permanently fitted on to a winch. The operation of this winch raises or lowers the derrick boom. The 'runner wire' runs through the

Single Swinging Derrick

upper and lower cargo blocks and the 'slewing wire' runs through slewing guy blocks on either side of the derrick. In its most basic form, the derrick is plumbed over the hatch square and secured. The cargo is then lifted with the runner blocks and the slewing guys are operated to swing the derrick and discharge the cargo over the side.

As the cargo purchase, the topping lift and the two guys must operate independently; four independent winches are needed to operate this type of derrick.

Union Purchase Derrick
One of the most efficient rigs is the Union Purchase Derrick, which is a rig

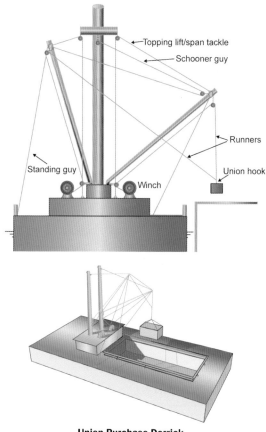

Union Purchase Derrick

where a pair of derricks are used in combination, the derricks being fixed and the cargo runners coupled.

One derrick plumbs the hatch and the other plumbs overside. The falls of the two derricks are fastened together at the cargo hook. One derrick boom is arranged over the hold and the other is overside. The booms are then fixed in position. When the vessel is discharging cargo, the derrick that is plumbing the hold lifts the load. After the load has been lifted over the hatch coamings, it is gradually transferred to the fall from the other derrick, which is plumbing overside. This is done by heaving on one fall and slacking on the other. Due to the coordination required in slacking one fall and heaving the other, only experienced operators must be employed. Union Purchase can become an extremely fast method of loading/discharging cargo in units of up to about 1½ tonnes each, but it has the disadvantage of placing heavy stresses on the outboard guys of both derricks, so additional static *preventer (standing) guys* are used. There is not a great deal of stress on the inboard guys, but these must be set taut to prevent the derrick jerking. As an alternative to inboard guys, a *schooner guy* may be rigged between the derrick boom heads, reducing deck clutter.

Precautions:
When using the derricks in the Union Purchase mode, the maximum load must not exceed either 1/3 the SWL of the lowest rated derrick in the pair or an absolute maximum of 2.5 tonnes.

Narrow angles between the outboard guys and the vertical should be avoided as this increases the load on them. However, the angle should not be too large as this increases the chance of the derrick jack-knifing. To avoid undue stresses on the rig, the angle between the falls should not exceed 90° and should never exceed 120°.

Doubling Gear
When using derricks in a Union Purchase Rig, the maximum load must not exceed 1/3 the SWL of the lowest rated derrick. Therefore, if there is a requirement to lift a load heavier than the SWL of the union rig, but less than that of the SWL of an individual derrick, the rig can be unhitched and the single derrick can be used as a swinging derrick. If the item's weight is close to or in excess of the SWL of the cargo runner, it may be lifted by *doubling up* the cargo runner so that the stress limit is not exceeded.

Doubling up the runner in this way will allow the lifting of a weight in excess of the SWL of the runner if rigged as a *single whip*. It does NOT, however, permit the lifting of a weight in excess of the SWL of the lifting appliance as a whole.

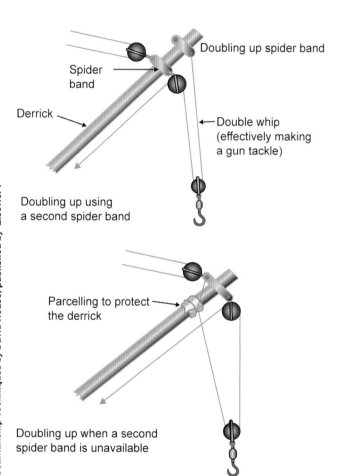

Spider band

Doubling up spider band

Derrick

Double whip
(effectively making
a gun tackle)

Doubling up using
a second spider band

Parcelling to protect
the derrick

Doubling up when a second
spider band is unavailable

Seamanship Techniques by David House, published by 'Elsevier'.

Velle Derrick

The Velle derrick is a patented derrick that was popular on general cargo vessels built in the 1970s. This is a single swinging derrick, the distinguishing feature of which is 'T' bar or 'floating bridle bar' at the derrick head to which the cargo hoist head blocks and topping spans blocks are secured. The advantage of this arrangement is that it allows a greater slewing radius and the 'T' bar provides stability when discharging or loading containers or heavy lifts.

There are two winches, each with separate barrels, control topping and slewing. Two lengths of wire are used leading from the topping winch barrels to the slewing winch barrels. On the topping winch, the barrels turn in the same direction and, on operation of either, the boom will top or lower. On the slewing winch barrels, they are wound in opposite directions and on operation the derrick slews, while maintaining the derrick head at a constant level. A third winch with twin barrels, both wound in the same direction, is used as the hoisting winch.

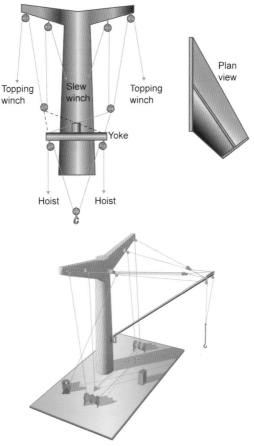

Traditional Velle Derrick Rig

Advantages:

- It is relatively easy to operate in comparison to a swinging derrick
- it is a one-man operation
- the 'T' bar helps to stabilise loads and prevents them from swinging
- there is less clutter compared to a traditional derrick
- the SWL is from 25 to 100 tonnes.

Hallen Derrick

The Hallen is another patented design in common use. This derrick has a 'D' frame mast with outrigger rods. The 'D' frame has the effect of maintaining a satisfactory angle between the twin topping lifts, allowing control and stability of the derrick when swung out over the ship's side, even to an angle of about 80° to the fore and aft line. The outrigger rods prevent contact between the topping lift pennants and the 'D' frame when the derrick is slewed to its maximum outboard angle.

Traditional Hallen Derrick Rig

Each topping lift has its own winch but both are usually controlled by one multi-position control. Topping is achieved by operating both winches in the same direction. Slewing is achieved by heaving on the winch at the side to which the derrick is to go, and slacking on the other. A third winch controls the cargo purchase. Alternatively, an arrangement similar to that employed by the Velle derrick can be used.

Advantages

- It is simple when compared to a single swinging derrick
- it uses a one-man operation of lifting, slewing and hoisting

- it operates with up to 15° of list
- it can operate down to 15° above the horizontal
- slewing angles are as much as 80°
- the deck area is clear of clutter
- it has up to 200 tonne capacity, with only the cargo hoist to be changed to operate quickly for lighter loads.

Stulken Heavy Lift Derrick
The Stulken derrick was patented in Germany in 1954 by Blohm & Voss. It has, since that time, has been fitted to hundreds of ships. The 'V' shaped inclined masts support the derrick and allow a wide arc of operation.

←Main deck

The derrick can be swung between the masts to service either of the two adjacent hatches.

Four winches operate the lifting plant, two for the hoist and one for each span. The hoisting winch has two gears to enable a faster operation when lifting relatively lighter loads.

One person can operate the derrick, either by using a remote control or by standing on a specially constructed platform.

Advantages:

- It is permanently rigged and so there is not much preparation time before use

- it has sealed bearings, which are low maintenance and reduce friction

- additional derricks suitable for a Union Purchase arrangement can be fixed on to the same inclined masts

- it is constructed of low weight high strength steel

- it is a one-man operation, using a remote if necessary

- safe working loads of up to 800 tonnes are possible.

Stulken Derridk

Pedestal Cranes

Shipboard pedestal cranes rotate on a pedestal and are permanently mounted. The main housing normally consists of the operator's cabin, winches and the jib, which projects from the pedestal. The crane is either electrically or hydraulically operated and the housing rotates on the pedestal. There are usually two winches inside the housing, one for the topping of the jib and the other for the hoist. Both are controlled from inside the cabin, using a joystick.

Advantages

- 360° rotation
- good spot loading
- fast operation
- low maintenance
- the SWL of two cranes may be combined when used together
- grabs, container spreaders etc can be fitted to the cargo hook.

Cargo purchase

Topping wire

Topping & hoisting motors & winches

Jib

Cargo hook

Operator's cab

Pedestal

www.mcgregor-group.com

Safety Features

- Limit switches for topping and hoisting
- jib angle indicator, indicates the angle of the jib that corresponds to the SWL
- two block limit switch, prevents the inadvertent contact of the floating runner block and the jib mounted runner block
- slack wire cut-off
- SWL cut-off prevents a weight in excess of the SWL from being lifted
- topping and hoisting winch cut-off, that cuts-off the power when less than 3 turns remain on the winches or if the wires become fouled
- a flashing light placed at the end of the jib to prevent accidental contact with shore cranes.

Shipboard Gantry Cranes

Gantry cranes have steel girders across the beam of a vessel, supported by legs and travelling on rails mounted on the ship's decks. The gantry houses the operator's cabin as well as the lifting mechanism, and it can travel athwartships on the bridge girders. The whole gantry can travel fore and aft on wheels mounted at the base. Hydraulic buffers at the ends of the rails prevent the crane from over-running the rails.

Shelters that allow the cargo operation to be carried out, even during light rain, can cover this type of crane. These are usually fitted onto ships loading and discharging weather critical cargo, such as plywood or paper products. Prior to bringing the crane into operation, hinged outriggers are swung out, allowing the discharge or loading of products over the ship's side. The outriggers are usually hydraulically operated and have a mechanism to lock them in place. Prior to sailing, the outriggers are folded in and locked onto the side of the girders.

The other type of gantry crane in use is the *jib type* crane. The main difference is the jib that is mounted on the bridge girders. In some types, the jib can travel athwartships along the bridge girders, while on other models the jib is fixed in the centre. In both cases, the jib swings from port to starboard and the operator's cabin is mounted on the jib. This type of gantry crane is used on small feeder container ships as the container spreader at the end of the jib can be used to load and discharge cargo from a very stable base.

Advantages of gantry cranes

- Mobile over the length of the deck
- unobstructed view for the operator

- shelters may be fitted to protect cargo during handling operations
- reduced possibility of load rotation due to box shaped girders
- fast operation possible with experienced operators.

Safety Features

- Klaxon and light when moving along the deck
- maximum safe trim cut-out
- emergency stop switch at deck level
- hydraulic buffer at the end of deck rails
- two block limit switch
- slack wire limit switch
- maximum SWL limit switch
- outrigger cut-outs if not locked in place
- 'cow-catcher' safety guards on the wheels, which cut out the power if they hit an obstruction.

KEY POINTS

- ♦ **Lifting plant must be checked prior to use and tested at regular intervals**
- ♦ **trained and certificated personnel must operate lifting plant**
- ♦ **cranes and derricks must be maintained as per manufacturers' instructions.**

Training and Certification

All cargo gear must only be operated by personnel who have received appropriate training in the operation of the plant. As a way of verification, a certificate may be issued. A risk assessment must be carried out prior to using the cargo gear for the first time and, based on the findings, appropriate control measures must be put in place.

Testing, Maintenance & Examination of Lifting Plant

Ships, cranes and derricks should be properly operated and maintained in accordance with manufacturers' instructions. Sufficient technical information must be available onboard, including the following:

- Rigging plans
- SWL of all fittings
- boom limiting angles
- manufacturers' instructions for replacing wires and sheaves.

Prior to use, a visual inspection must be carried out looking for the following:

- Any leaks of hydraulic oil
- worn or damaged wires
- excessive corrosion
- cracking at welds
- missing marking.

All control units, joysticks, alarms and limit switches must be checked prior to use and all controls must be operated before attaching the slings or grabs to the crane or derrick. Any slings to be used must be inspected and must be of sufficient SWL.

Banksman

Trained personnel should direct the lifting plant operator using agreed and generally understood means of communication. The Code of Safe Working Practices for Merchant Seamen (COSWP) contains a list of approved hand signals that must be used.

Testing & Certification

The *'Merchant Shipping (Provision and Use of Work Equipment) Regulations 2006'* requires the following, in accordance with manufacturer's instructions, for testing and certification of the Lifting Plant:

- A test using an approved proof load, which may be greater than the SWL of the lifting plant, must be carried out:
    - after manufacture and installation of the plant
    - after repair or modification likely to affect SWL or the strength or stability of the equipment
    - at maximum intervals of 5 years

- a thorough examination, in accordance with the manufacturer's instructions, must be carried out by a competent person:
  - after installation and before being put into service for the first time
  - after assembly at a new site or location
  - in accordance with an examination scheme
  - at least every 6 months for equipment for lifting persons
  - at least every 12 months
  - after a statutory test
  - under any exceptional circumstances likely to jeopardise safety of the equipment.

Certificates & Reports

The Master must ensure that a certificate or report is onboard within 28 days of any statutory test or examination and that the certificate remains onboard for at least two years following the receipt of the next certificate. Certificates and reports should be kept readily available onboard and copies of the latest certificates should be made available to any shore worker using the ship's lifting plant.

Certificates and reports should be in the form approved by the Secretary of State and based on the internationally agreed form prepared by the International Labour Organization (ILO).

A *Register of Lifting Appliances and Cargo Handling Gear* should be maintained in a form recommended by the ILO as shown in COSWP. The register may be in paper or electronic form.

Further details are provided in MGN 332 (Lifting Operations and Lifting Equipment).

Marking of Lifting Equipment

The employer must ensure that each lifting appliance and item of lifting gear is clearly marked with:

- Its SWL
- a means of identification.

Where the SWL of a crane varies with operating radius, an indicator clearly showing the SWL at any given radius must be fitted.

The SWL of an appliance that is normally used with a specific attachment, eg a spreader or clamp, should specify whether the weight of the attachment is included in the SWL. Any item of lifting gear weighing a significant proportion of the overall SWL must be clearly marked with its weight in addition to its SWL. Slings supplied in batches must bear the same identification mark.

Annex 7.1

CERTIFICATE OF TEST AND THOROUGH
EXAMINATION OF LIFTING APPLIANCES

Name of Ship   Certificate No. ....

Official Number

Call sign

Port of Registry

Name of Owner

(1) Situation and description of lifting application (with distinguishing numbers or marks, if any) which have been tested and thoroughly examined	(2) Angle to the horizontal or radius at which test load applied	(3) Test load (tonnes)	(4) Safe working load (SWL) at angle or radius shown in column (2) (tonnes)

Name and address of the firm or competent
person who witnessed testing and carried out
thorough examination

....
....
....

I certify that on the date to which I have appended my signature, the gear shown in column (1) was tested and thoroughly examined and no defects or permanent deformation were found; and that the safe working load is as shown.

Date: ....   Signature: ....

Place: ....

Note: This certificate is the standard international form as recommended by the International Labour Office in accordance with ILO Convention No. 152.

Code of Safe Working Practices for Merchant Seamen, TSO

KEY POINTS

♦ **A risk assessment must be done prior to a heavy lift**

♦ **the critical stage is when the weight has been lifted off the ground by the ship's lifting gear**

♦ **it is important to have adequate stability prior to the operation and to avoid any slack tanks.**

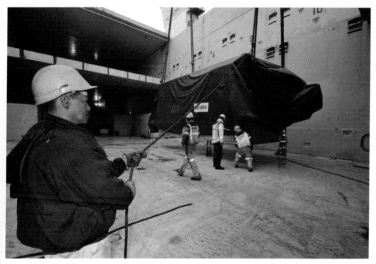

Loading Heavy Cargo

A heavy lift operation must always be well planned and carried out with the utmost care. A risk assessment must be carried out and a permit to work system must be in operation. In any heavy lift operation, the critical stage, when using ship's lifting gear, is when the load has just cleared the ground. The weight of the load then acts as if it has been placed on top of the lifting gear and this causes a rise in the ship's centre of gravity. Initial stability must be adequate to avoid a situation where the ship's centre of gravity rises above its transverse metacentre, causing a capsizing lever to form. The ship will also heel when the load is lifted up and any slack tanks will create a free surface effect, causing a further rise in the centre of gravity. The entire operation must be carried out slowly and using experienced operators. The lifting hook must be exactly above the load to avoid the load dragging on the ground and swinging, causing excessive strain

33

on the lifting gear. The Port Authority must be informed before the operation so that any passing traffic can be asked to slow down. The following is a list of things to check before and during this critical operation:

- Ensure the vessel is as near as possible to upright and calculate the minimum GM and maximum heel during operation
- avoid any slack tanks
- lay out dunnage to spread the load and protect the ship/cargo
- check deck or tank top load limit
- lifting gear certificates must be in order and the SWL sufficient.
- lifting points must be satisfactory
- any slings used must have an adequate SWL

- steadying lines are to be attached to prevent the load swinging
- the accommodation ladder/ gangway is to be attended
- sufficient crew, wearing PPE, to attend to mooring lines
- fenders rigged and barges, etc cast off
- railings removed if required
- adequate power on deck
- communications established
- non-essential personnel are cleared from the working area
- operators are fully certificated
- lifting hook is plumb above the load
- weight must be taken slowly
- relevant signals should be displayed and the Port Authority informed.

1.13 The Cargo Stowage & Securing Code (CSS)

The general principles of stowage and securing of cargoes, as described in the CSS Code, are as follows:

- Cargoes are to be stowed and secured so that the ship and persons on board are not at risk

- stowage and securing should be planned, executed and monitored properly

Cargo Stowage and Securing Code

- personnel carrying out the tasks should be qualified and experienced

- personnel planning and executing the tasks should have a sound practical knowledge of the application and content of the Ship's *Cargo Securing Manual*[1]

- improper stowage and securing will be hazardous to other cargoes and the ship

- stowage and securing must be planned with the most severe weather conditions that could be expected on the voyage in mind

- ship handling decisions in bad weather must be carefully considered.

The CSS Code lists the following criteria for estimating the risk of a cargo shift:

- The dimensional and physical properties of the cargo

- location of the cargo and the stowage onboard

- suitability of the ship for the cargo

- suitability of the securing arrangements

- expected seasonal weather conditions

- expected ship behaviour during the voyage

- stability of the ship

- geographical area of the voyage

- duration of the voyage.

These criteria, along with the fact that some cargoes have a tendency to

See section 1.13.2

compact themselves during the voyage or have a low coefficient of friction, must be taken into account when selecting suitable stowage and securing methods. The Master should only accept cargoes if he is satisfied that they can be safely carried.

After evaluating the risk of the cargo shifting, the Master should ensure, prior to loading, that:

- The deck area is clean and free of grease and oil
- the cargo is in a suitable condition for transport
- all necessary cargo securing equipment is on board

- cargo that is either in or on cargo transport units or vehicles is properly secured to those vehicles or units.

The CSS Code, in line with SOLAS Chapters VI and VII, requires the carriage onboard of an approved *Cargo Securing Manual*. The cargo securing arrangements in this manual should be based on the forces expected to affect the cargo carried by the ship, calculated either in accordance with the method described in Annex 13 of the CSS Code or an acceptable alternative.

1.13.1 Structure of Cargo Stowage and Securing Code

Chapter 1
General information including definitions, forces, cargo behaviour, cargo equipment and the required shipment information.

Chapter 2
Details the principles of safe stowage and securing of cargoes. This deals with the following points:

- Suitability of cargo for transport
- cargo distribution
- cargo securing arrangements
- residual strength after wear and tear
- friction forces
- shipboard supervision and inspection.

Chapters 3 and 4
Standardised and semi-standardised stowage and securing.
Includes securing arrangements for the stowage and securing of vehicles.

Chapter 5
Non-standardised stowage and securing.
This includes advice for cargoes not covered by chapters 3 and 4, particularly cargoes which are difficult to stow or have proven to be a potential source of danger. These include cargoes such as:

- Containers on non-cellular ships
- portable tanks and receptacles
- special wheel based cargoes
- heavy cargoes
- coiled sheet steel
- heavy metal products
- anchor chains
- scrap metal in bulk

- flexible intermediate bulk containers
- logs in under deck stow.

Chapter 6
Actions to be taken in heavy weather and advice on the measures to avoid excessive acceleration:

- Alteration of course or speed
- heaving to
- early avoidance of areas of adverse weather
- timely ballasting and deballasting to improve the ship's behaviour
- voyage planning to avoid areas of severe weather and sea conditions.

Chapter 7
Actions that may be taken once a cargo has shifted. The Code recommends the following actions for consideration:

- Alterations of course
- reductions of speed
- monitoring the integrity of the ship
- restowing or resecuring the cargo
- increasing friction
- diversion of route or seeking shelter.

Annex 12
Safe stowage and securing of cargoes that are a potential source of danger, as detailed in Chapter 5 of the Code.

Annex 13
Methods to assess the efficiency of securing arrangements for non-standardised cargoes, including the provision of guidance for the preparation of the Cargo Securing Manual.

Annex 13 also gives a rule-of-thumb method for securing cargoes:

"The total of the Maximum Securing Load (MSL) values of the securing devices on each side of a unit of cargo (port as well as starboard) should equal the weight of the unit".

This method does not take into account the adverse effects of lashing angles, non-homogenous distribution of forces among the securing devices or the favourable effect of friction. The Code recommends that the transverse lashing angles to the deck should not be greater than 60° and that adequate friction is provided by the use of suitable materials.

The Code recommends a *safety factor* to be used in calculations to take into account the possibility of uneven distribution of forces among the devices or reduced capability due to improper assembly of the devices. The safety factor gives the calculated strength (CS) from the MSL:

$$CS = \frac{MSL}{Safety\,Factor}$$

Maximum securing load is a term used to define the allowable load capacity for a device used to secure cargo to a ship. Safe working load (SWL) may be substituted for the MSL provided this is equal to or exceeds the strength defined by MSL.

SOLAS Chapters VI and VII requires a Cargo Securing Manual (CSM) to be onboard all types of ships, other than solid and liquid bulk, engaged in the carriage of cargoes.

Cargo units and cargo transport units must be loaded, stowed and secured throughout the voyage in accordance with this manual.

For UK flag vessels, SI 336 *Carriage of Cargoes Regulations* state that:

"All passenger ships and cargo ships carrying cargoes other than solid bulk cargoes, except cargo ships of less than 500 tons engaged on voyages which are not international voyages, shall carry on board a Cargo Securing Manual".

The approved Cargo Securing Manual must conform to the guidelines developed by the IMO. All securing devices must meet acceptable functional and strength criteria applicable to the ship and its cargo. All crew engaged in the stowage and securing of cargo must be trained and instructed in the safe and efficient operation of the lashing and securing devices.

Key Definitions:

Maximum Securing Load (MSL) is a term used to define the allowable load

Cargo Securing Manual

capacity for a device used to secure cargo to a ship.

Safe Working Load (SWL) may be substituted for MSL for securing purposes, provided this is equal to or exceeds the strength defined by MSL.

Standardised Cargo means cargo for which the ship is provided with an approved securing system, based upon cargo units of specific types.

Semi-standardised Cargo means cargo for which the ship is provided with a securing system capable of accommodating a limited variety of cargo units, such as vehicles, trailers, etc.

Non-standardised Cargo means cargo that requires individual stowage and securing arrangements.

Securing a Container on Deck

Chapter 1 contains general statements dealing with the requirement to practise good seamanship and the requirement to maintain all securing devices to a good standard. It also specifies a minimum quantity of spares to be carried on board.

Chapter 2 provides details of the specifications of fixed and portable securing devices and their maintenance schemes. This should give as much detail as possible about the securing devices in use on that ship. Plans or sketches can be used to illustrate the type, location and total number of securing devices on board.

Chapter 3 provides handling and safety instructions and an evaluation of the

forces acting on the cargo transport units using tables and diagrams of those forces acting on the cargo in relation to the metacentric height. This chapter also draws the Master's attention to the correct application of portable securing devices, taking into account factors such as:

- Duration of the voyage
- geographical area of the voyage, with particular regard to the minimum safe operational temperature of the portable securing devices
- sea conditions that may be expected
- dimensions, design and characteristics of the ship
- expected static and dynamic forces during the voyage

- type and packaging of cargo units, including vehicles
- intended stowage pattern of the cargo unit, including vehicles' mass and the dimensions of the cargo units and vehicles.

Chapter 4 contains handling, safety, stowage and securing instructions for containers and other standardised cargoes. It illustrates allowable stowage patterns, evaluation of forces acting on cargo transport units and principles of stowage and securing both on deck and under deck. Stowage and securing plans must be available illustrating, among other things, stowage patterns, the maximum stack weight limitations and permitted stack heights.

It contains further information on the nominal increase of forces or accelerations with an increase of initial stability. Recommendations should be given for reducing the risk of cargo losses from deck stowage by restrictions to stack masses or stack heights where high initial stability cannot be avoided.

Inspection and maintenance schemes, as required by the IMO guidelines, can be contained in a separate document provided this is clearly referenced in the Cargo Securing Manual. Ship specific handling and safety instructions must be included and these should contain the results of a risk assessment, if one was carried out.

The shipper is also required to supply cargo specific information to the Master so that he can evaluate the suitability of the cargo for the ship and make decisions on the stowage and securing.

KEY POINTS

♦ Timber cargoes carried on deck can shift and cause damage to vessels and can result in the ship capsizing

♦ international rules are in place to safely stow and carry timber cargoes on deck.

(Courtesy of MCA)

MV Ice Prince. Loss of Timber Deck Cargo

In response to a increasing number of incidents of casualties related to a shift of timber cargo carried on deck, the IMO published the *'Code of Safe Practice for Ships Carrying Timber Deck Cargoes'*. This publication must be onboard all UK vessels, as per *SI 336 Carriage of Cargoes Regulations (1999)*.

The purpose of the Code is to make recommendations on stowage, securing and other safety matters related to the carriage of timber on deck. The Code applies to ships of length greater than 24 metres.

Key Definitions
Timber means sawn wood or lumber, cants, logs, poles, pulpwood and all other type of timber in loose or packaged forms. The term does not include wood pulp or similar cargo.

Timber deck cargo means a cargo of timber carried on an uncovered part of a freeboard or superstructure deck.

Code of Safe Practice for Ships Carrying Timber Deck Cargoes, 1991

Timber load line means a special load line assigned to ships complying with certain conditions related to their construction as set out in the *International Convention on Load Lines.* It is used when the cargo complies with the stowage and securing conditions of the *Code of Safe Practice for Ships Carrying Timber Deck Cargoes.*

Weather deck means the uppermost complete deck exposed to weather and sea.

Stability Requirements

The ship should be supplied with comprehensive stability information that takes into account the timber deck cargo. This should enable the Master to quickly obtain accurate guidance as to the stability of the ship under varying conditions of service. Comprehensive rolling period tables or diagrams have proved to be a very useful aid in verifying the actual stability conditions.

The stability at all times should be positive and the following should be among the factors to be taken into account.

The increased weight of the timber deck cargo due to:

- absorption of water in dried or seasoned timber
- ice accretion, if applicable
- variations in consumables, such as oil or water
- the free surface effect of liquid in tanks
- weight of water trapped in broken spaces within the timber deck cargo and especially logs.

Before proceeding to sea, the Master should ensure that:

- bridge visibility is unobstructed
- the ship is upright
- the ship has an adequate metacentric height
- the ship meets the required stability criteria
- wind heeling has been accounted for.

Loading should cease immediately if an unexplained list develops. The *Merchant Shipping (Load Line) Regulations 1998* allow an initial GM of 0.05 metres, provided the timber is stowed and secured as per the Code. This is because the buoyancy of timber contributes to the reserve buoyancy of the ship and so the ship can sail with a lower initial GM. Excessive stability should also be avoided as this creates racking stresses and increases the stresses on the lashing and securing system. The Code recommends that the metacentric height should, by preference, not exceed 3% of the beam, although this can vary from ship to ship.

Some ships are allocated with timber load lines. Such ships are only allowed to load to this load line provided the lashing and securing requirements of the Code and the applicable regulations of the Load Line Convention are followed *(The Merchant Shipping (Load Line) Regulations 1998, Part IV).*

Stowage Considerations

The *'Code of Safe Practice for Ships Carrying Timber Deck Cargoes'* recommends the following to be checked prior to loading timber on the weather deck:

- Hatch covers, and other openings to spaces below that area, should be securely closed and battened down
- air pipes and ventilators should be efficiently protected and check valves or similar devices should be examined to ascertain their effectiveness against the entry of water
- accumulations of ice and snow on such areas should be removed
- to have all deck lashings, uprights, etc in position before loading. This will be necessary should a pre-loading examination of securing equipment be required in the loading port
- ensure that access to all areas of the ship regularly used in the necessary working of the ship is not impeded.

During loading, the timber deck cargo should be kept free of any accumulations of ice and snow. On completion of loading, but before sailing, a thorough inspection of the ship should be carried out. Soundings should also be taken to verify that no structural damage has occurred, causing ingress of water.

The height of timber cargo should be restricted to ensure that:

- adequate visibility is assured
- a safe margin of stability is maintained at all stages of the voyage
- cargo does not overhang the ship side

- the weight of the timber deck cargo does not exceed the designed maximum permissible load on the weather deck and hatches.

For ships provided with, and making use of, their timber load lines, the cargo should be stowed so as to extend:

- over the entire available length of the well or wells between superstructures and as close as practicable to end bulkheads
- at least to the after end of the aftermost hatchway in the case where there is no limiting superstructure at the aft end
- athwartships as close as possible to the ship sides, after making due allowance for obstructions such as guard rails, bulwark stays, uprights, pilot boarding access, etc. This is provided that any area of broken stowage thus created at the side of the ship does not exceed a mean of 4% of the breadth
- to at least the standard height of a superstructure other than a raised quarterdeck
- to meet the requirements of the approved stability manual.

The basic principle is that there should be a solid stow during all stages of the loading process. This can only be achieved by the constant supervision of responsible officers.

Securing
Every lashing should pass over the timber deck cargo and be shackled to independent eye plates that are adequate for the intended purpose, and then efficiently attached to the deck

stringer plate or other strengthened points. They should be installed in such a manner as to be, as far as is practicable, in contact with the timber deck cargo throughout its full height.

All lashings and components used for securing should:

- possess a breaking strength of not less than 133 kN[1]
- after initial stressing, show an elongation of not more than 5% at 80% of their breaking strength
- show no permanent deformation after having been subjected to a proof load of not less than 40% of their original breaking strength.

Every lashing should be provided with a tightening device or systems placed to safely and efficiently operate when required. The load to be produced by the tightening device or system should not be less than:

- 27 kN in the horizontal part
- 16 kN in the vertical part.

After completion of lashing, there should be at least half the threaded length of screw available for tightening during the voyage. The spacing of the lashings should be such that the two lashings at each end of each length of continuous deck stow are positioned as close as is practicable to the extreme end of the timber deck cargo.

Timber uprights should be fitted when required by the nature, height or type of timber carried. When fitted, uprights should be:

- of adequate strength
- fitted at intervals not exceeding 3 metres
- secured adequately to the deck.

Lashings should be spaced depending on the height of the cargo:

- for a height of 4 m and below, the spacing should be 3 m
- for heights of above 4 m, the spacing should be 1.5 m.

Rounded angle pieces of suitable material and design should be used along the upper outboard edge of the stow to bear the stress of the lashings.

If the timber deck cargo is stowed over the hatches and higher, it should, in addition to being secured by the lashings recommended, be in a system of athwartship lashings (*hog lashings*) joining each port and starboard pair of uprights near the top of the stow and at other appropriate levels as appropriate for the height of the stow.

A lashing system to tighten the stow, where a dual continuous wire rope (*wiggle wire*) is passed from side to side over the cargo and held continuously through a

[1] One Newton equals 0.225 lbs force or 0.1 kgf.

Wiggle Wire Securing Arrangement

Typical lashing system for deck cargo of cants

series of snatch blocks, can also be used. The dual continuous wire rope should be led to a winch or other tensioning device to facilitate further tightening. This can also be used as a quick release mechanism in order to jettison the cargo in case of an emergency.

All lashings and securing devices used must be tested and certified. A record must be maintained of all certificates, testing and inspection dates. As per the recommendations of the Code, lashing plans must be provided to the ship and these must be available for inspection.

On completion of lashing, a walkway or other means of access must be provided to other areas of the ship without endangering the lives of crewmembers.

Prior to sailing and immediately after sailing, all lashings must be examined and tightened as the vibration of the ship may have caused them to loosen. Records of all checks and adjustments to lashings must be maintained in the ship's logbook.

The Master must ensure that proper weather routeing is carried out to avoid areas of bad weather and high swell. If bad weather causes the jettisoning or loss of cargo, appropriate reports must be made to the nearest coastal state as per Chapter V of SOLAS.

KEY POINTS

♦ **Containerisation and door to door transport have revolutionised world trade**

♦ **correct securing and stowage of containers and cargoes within containers is vitally important.**

One of the most important ship types to come into existence after World War II was the container ship. The man credited with starting the container revolution is Malcolm McLean, a road transport operator from the US. He converted two tankers to carry trailers and sailed from New York to Houston in 1956[1]. Since then, containerisation has revolutionised world trade and commerce as the benefits of containerisation over general cargo ships are many. The cargo in the container can be transported from door to door and this has reduced warehousing costs and increased security in transit. Time in port is minimised and port labour costs are also reduced due to the lower numbers of people required for loading and unloading a cellular container ship. The main disadvantages are the increased capital costs in building specialised ships and terminals and the increased investment in specialised IT systems to track and locate containers.

Ship sizes have increased substantially in the past few years and ships of more than 8,000 TEU[2] are increasingly common. It has been predicted that, by 2010, several ships with a capacity of 15,000 TEUs will be in operation. They will be up to 450 metres long, 70 metres wide and will carry 24 rows of containers. With the ship size increasing, there has been a corresponding increase in incidents of cargo losses due to containers being swept overboard in bad weather. The wide variety of container types can also create a problem as the biggest container ship can carry more refrigerated cargoes than a conventional reefer ship, and more chemical and dangerous cargoes than a small chemical tanker.

Container sizes have been standardised since the 1960s and, except for a few specialised types of containers, the majority of containers are of either 20 feet by 8 feet by 8 1/2 feet or 40 feet by 8 feet by 8 1/2 feet. The majority of container ships in existence are *cellular ships*. This means that the containers fit in slots under deck and do not need additional lashing or securing if carried under deck. A few conventional ships are also able to carry containers but they need to be secured under deck using chains or wires.

[1] http://www.oceansatlas.com/transportation/dry-cargo-ships
[2] TEU: Twenty foot equivalent unit, this is the amount of empty twenty foot boxes that the ship can carry and is a measurement of volume.

Standard Container Types

20 Foot Dry

Dimensions of general purpose container	Weight: 2300 Kgs

20 ft standard 20' x 8' x 8'6"

Weight: 2300 Kgs
Max Payload: 28180 Kg
Max Gross weight: 30480 Kg
Cubic Capacity: 33.2 m³

40 Foot Dry

Dimensions of general purpose container

40 ft standard 40' x 8' x 8'6"

Weight: 3750 Kgs
Max Payload: 28750 Kg
Max Gross weight: 32500 Kg
Cubic Capacity: 67.7 m³

40 Foot High Cube

Dimensions of general purpose container

40 ft standard 40' x 8' x 9'6"

Dimensions similar
to above except
the height is 9'6"
Cubic Capacity: 76.4 m³

20 Foot Reefer

Dimensions of general reefer container

20 ft standard 20' x 8' x 8'6"

Dimensions similar to the
20 foot dry container above,
except the cubic capacity
reduces to 28.3 m³ due to
insulation.

Container Stowage

Containers are mainly stowed lengthwise as the loading capacity of the side walls is greater than the ends. Also, in a seaway, the stresses are usually greater athwartships than in a fore and aft direction. On some conventional ships, containers may be stowed athwartships. Care must be taken to ensure access between containers for checking, lashing and unloading. Containers, when stowed on deck, are exposed to the stresses caused by the vessel moving in a seaway and are also exposed to wind stresses. The main principle of container stowage is to ensure a compact stow in all cases.

In a semi-automatic twistlock, a spring-loaded mechanism automatically locks the twistlock in place. Other containers in the same tier have intermediate twistlocks fitted that lock them onto the container immediately below. The containers are then held together over the entire width of the ship or the hatch-cover, using cross lashings tightened by turnbuckles.

To complete the stow, *bridge fittings* may be fitted on the top row. These are attached to adjoining containers and compact the stow. However, on modern ships, bridge fittings have become rare as the heights of stows have increased, making it dangerous to manually fit bridge fittings on the top tier.

Securing Mechanisms

Manual Twistlock

**Securing Bridge Fitting
to Container Top**

Any lashing system must be approved by the Flag State or a designated Classification Society. All approved lashing systems will be found in the *Cargo Securing Manual,* along with the maintenance procedures. On conventional vessels, additional lashing equipment may also be used.

Loading into Cell Guides

For under deck stowage on cellular ships, *cell guides* are constructed from the tank top to the top of the hold. These guides are the width of a standard container and the boxes are slotted in place. Usually no other lashing is required, perhaps with the exception of stacking cones between container tiers.

For conventional ships adapted to carry containers, a number of different systems are in existence. Since the holds are not adapted to carry containers, they have to be lashed using bridge fittings and cross lashed using chains. The following diagram from *The Container Handbook*[3] illustrates underdeck lashing of containers on a conventional ship using bridge fittings, stacking cones, twistlocks and chain lashings for the bottom two tiers.

Container Stowage Planning

It is important to be able to locate the position of each individual container onboard a ship to effectively plan the loading and discharging. To enable this, containers are usually stowed following the *bay-row-tier* method. The ship is divided lengthwise into bays, which are numbered from fore towards aft in the following manner:

Tiers are numbered in the following manner:

On deck, the bottom tier is numbered '82', the one above is tier 84 and so on.

Odd numbered bays are for 20 foot containers while even numbered bays are for 40 foot containers. One 40 foot bay can be divided into two 20 foot bays. For example, if the stowage plan refers to Bay 02 then the container in question is 40 foot in length but if the plan refers to Bay 01 or Bay 03, the container is 20 foot in length.

To plan athwartships stowage, the containers are divided into *rows and tiers*. The rows of containers on a ship are numbered with even numbers from the centre towards the port side and odd numbers from the centre towards the starboard side. If there are an odd number of rows, the centre row is numbered '00'.

Underdeck the bottom tier is tier '02' the one above tier 04 and so on as illustrated in the following diagram.

The containers are always referred to in the 'bay-row-tier' format. For example, using the above diagram a 20 foot container stowed underdeck (shaded) will be referred to as Bay 53, Row 12, Tier 12; or 531212 in short. On deck, the shaded container on Bay 54 (40 feet) will be referred to as 540788; and the 20 foot box on Bay 55 will be 551184.

To illustrate the containers on a cargo plan, *bay plans* are used. Each bay plan shows the cell and a tier number for each container space and provides

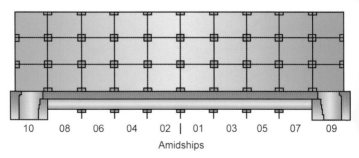

10   08   06   04   02 | 01   03   05   07   09

Amidships

Bay 53/54

16 14 12 10 08 06 04 02 00 01 03 05 07 09 11 13 15

Bay 55

16 14 12 10 08 06 04 02 00 01 03 05 07 09 11 13 15

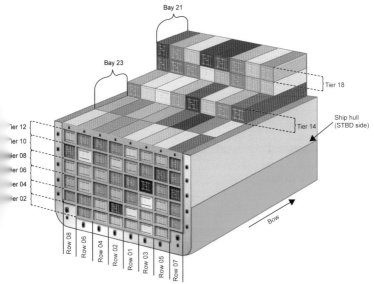

Bay 21

Bay 23

Tier 18

Ship hull
(STBD side)

Tier 14

Tier 12
Tier 10
Tier 08
Tier 06
Tier 04
Tier 02

Bow

Row 08 Row 06 Row 04 Row 02 Row 01 Row 03 Row 05 Row 07

Container Identification System

space for container codes and weight information. The container codes help to identify the container in that space. The weight information helps the planner distribute the weight of the containers and enter this into the stability computer. Container codes consist of a port code, a container serial number and the container weight.

- check that any over-height or over-width cargoes are properly stowed
- check lashings for breakbulk cargo stowed on containers
- check that stack limits are not exceeded
- note any physical damage to the containers and evidence of security breach

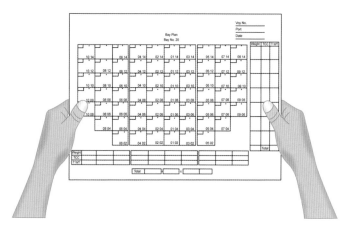

Duties of the OOW

Issues and items that the OOW must consider when loading containers include:

- Understand and review the stowage plan
- be aware of special requirements for containers containing dangerous goods, including their stowage, segregation and marking
- reefer containers are to be placed in their correct slots and their temperatures monitored as per the manifest

- check that the door seal is intact
- check for leaks or other evidence of cargo damage
- ensure that the lashing plan is correctly followed
- attend to the ballast to ensure that the ship remains upright and with reasonable trim by the stern
- check all lashings on completion
- keep proper records
- ensure the Ship Security Plan (SSP) is adhered to.

KEY POINTS

- ♦ **On a Ro Ro vessel, correct stowage and securing of wheeled cargo is vital for safety reasons**
- ♦ **HMSO publishes a code of practice that provides guidance and information on safe procedures to be followed on board these vessels.**

Lashing Freight Cargo on Car Deck

Cargo stowage and securing is a vital aspect of Ro Ro vessel operations. To reduce the risks inherent in the loading, securing and carriage of cargoes on such vessels, guidelines are given in the "*Roll-on/Roll-off Ships – Stowage and Securing of Vehicles – Code of Practice*" published by HMSO. The *Code of Safe Practice for Cargo Stowage and Securing (CSS Code)* published by the IMO, also gives guidance on securing and stowage of all cargo. It is mandatory that this is carried onboard UK flag vessels. The ship should also have on board an approved *Cargo Securing Manual,* in accordance with Regulations VI/5 and VII/6 of SOLAS 1974.

Principal sources of danger on board Ro Ro vessels

These can be classified into four broad areas:

- Ship related
- cargo related
- lashing and securing related
- personnel related.

Ship related dangers and means of preventing

1. Poorly maintained ramps, lifts and bow and stern doors. Retractable car-decks, ramps and lifting appliances should be of sound construction, fitted with appropriate fencing and tested by a competent person. A planned maintenance system should be in operation.

2. Poorly maintained, inadequately illuminated or badly planned decks. Adequate permanent lighting should be provided to illuminate vehicle decks, ramps and lifting appliances. Lights are to be positioned so as to reduce to a minimum the shadow areas caused by stowed vehicles.

3. Wet decks. Adequate availability of equipment to deal with spillage, eg drip trays or absorbent material. Decks to be kept as dry as possible.

4. Inadequate securing points. The ship should be provided with an adequate number of securing points of a sufficient strength. Enough cargo securing gear should be available, as detailed in the vessel's Cargo Securing Manual. The duration of the voyage and the type of cargo must be taken into account when designing the securing arrangements.

Cargo related dangers and means of preventing

1. The unsatisfactory condition or design of vehicles presented for shipment in terms of inadequate number of securing points, inadequate strength of the securing points, ineffective braking system. Pre-load inspection should be carried out and systems must be in place to reject unsuitable cargo.

2. Cargo in freight containers or in trailers badly stowed or overloaded. Container or vehicle packing certificates must be obtained and a pre-load inspection carried out where possible.

3. Free surface effect in tank vehicles and tank containers that are slack. Margins must be added to stability calculations for free surface effect when loading tank vehicles full of liquid, and must be confirmed by calculation before departure.

4. Vehicles being moved negligently on vehicle decks and ramps. Adequate systems to be in place to prevent negligent movement of vehicles on decks and ramps. Particular caution must be taken in the movement of foot passengers between vehicles.

5. Failure to apply the handbrakes. After loading, a nominated crewmember should check that the handbrakes are applied.

6. Excess free play in vehicle suspensions. This will affect lashings as they may come loose due to the movement of the vehicle suspensions in a seaway. In the case of air suspensions in larger vehicles, air is often drained out prior to lashing them.

7. Failure to comply with the IMDG code. Prior to loading vehicles or trailers with dangerous goods, a dangerous goods note and a vehicle packing certificate is needed. The goods must be stowed, lashed and segregated as per the IMDG Code and only in spaces allowed by the vessel's Document of Compliance for loading dangerous goods.

Lashing and securing related dangers

Lashing and securing points must be adequate and the lashing material onboard must be as per the vessel's approved *Cargo Securing Manual*. The lashing plan must take into account the type and duration of the voyage and the lashings must be monitored and tightened at regular intervals. All securing must be completed before the vessel proceeds out to sea. Freight vehicles over 3.5 tonnes, dangerous goods and livestock must be secured in all circumstances when expected conditions are such that movement of the vehicles relative to the ship can be expected. Lashings should not be released for unloading before the vessel is secured to the berth unless expressly ordered by the Master. A planned maintenance system must be in place for the lashing equipment and adequate records must be available for inspection.

The movement, stowage and securing of vehicles must be under the close supervision of a responsible officer. Vehicles should, so far as is possible, be stowed in a fore and aft manner. Vehicles should not obstruct access to emergency escapes and bow and stern doors, and must not be stowed across water curtains.

Personnel related dangers and means of preventing

1. Poor traffic management on and of the decks and ramps. The movement, storage and securing must be under the supervision of a responsible deck officer, who must have clear and direct communication with deck crew and shore staff.

2. Risk of injury due to moving vehicles. Separating the means of access of passengers and vehicles should eliminate this. Supervisors must use clear and proper signals. All personnel engaged in the cargo operation should wear hi-visibility clothing and PPE. Passengers must not be allowed on vehicle decks prior to the safe berthing of the vessel. Clear markings and notices, warning of the dangers of remaining on vehicle decks, must be in place on pedestrian walkways.

3. Slips, trips and falls. Decks must be kept free of oil and grease. Adequate illumination must be available at all times.

4. Risk of suffocation due to exhaust gases. Engines must be switched off as soon as possible and the ventilation system must be in operation at all times during cargo operation. The oxygen levels in the air must be continually monitored using fixed or portable indicators.

KEY POINTS

♦ **Reefer cargoes require special care due to their perishable nature**

♦ **safe carriage depends on maintaining suitable storage conditions during transportation.**

Reefer Vessel

Refrigerated cargoes include both frozen and chilled goods, the latter including fresh fruits and vegetables. Generally, frozen goods do not suffer if over-cooled, while chilled goods can be damaged by low temperatures, either by freezing or by chilling injury to the fresh produce. Many chilled cargoes are damaged if subjected to temperatures below that experienced in the growing area.

Successful transportation depends on the following factors:

• Shipper carriage instructions

• crew knowledge of the refrigeration plant

• preparation of hold spaces to the required standard

• continuous monitoring of the hold atmosphere.

Shipper carriage instructions

The responsibility for specifying carriage instructions belongs to the shipper, who is the owner of the goods. Only the shipper knows the full nature of the goods and their requirements. The exact nature of the cargo needs to be known. In the case of fruit, for example, carriage requirements may vary dependent on type, variety, maturity, origin and growing season conditions. Shipper's instructions should also specify the ventilation, stowage humidity and segregation needs.

Carriage instructions should be supplied to the ship well in advance so that the crew can begin preparations in good time. Onboard record keeping is vital for reefer cargoes to protect the shipowner from expensive cargo damage claims and provide proof that the crew complied with the shipper's instructions.

Types of refrigeration plants

Types of refrigeration plant in common use are:

1. Direct expansion grid cooling

- cooling can be continued throughout cargo operations.

Disadvantages:

- Variations in grid temperatures due to ship movement
- problems with leakage
- frosting can occur on the grids
- may have problems fitting grids around holds and hatch covers

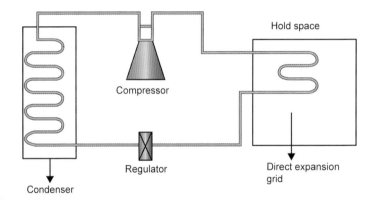

The refrigerant gas is compressed/ condensed and passed through a piping system that is attached to the bulkheads and deck heads of the cargo space. Heat is transferred to the coolant passing through the pipelines and is then led back to the refrigerant plant.

Advantages:

- Cheapest method of cooling chambers
- cooling grids are fixed at the source of heat ingress

- usually only commercially viable for a smaller ship.

2. Brine battery cooling system

In this system, brine[1] is cooled using a conventional refrigeration system and the cooled brine is then circulated, using the brine pump via fixed pipelines, around the holds. Air is then blown across the cold brine and circulated through the hold. The salinity of the solution can be adjusted in order to lower the freezing point of the brine.

[1] Water saturated with or containing large amounts of a salt, especially sodium chloride or calcium chloride

Brine battery

Compressor

Hold

Regulator

Brine tank

Fan

Condenser

Brine pump

Advantages:

- No need to circulate expensive refrigerant gas throughout the holds
- easier to control temperature as less pipelines contain the refrigerant
- no possibility of gas leaks in the hold
- brine is relatively inexpensive to replace in case of leaks
- brine can be heated or cooled to allow for a range of temperatures.

Disadvantages:

- Expensive to install, with high capital costs
- air trunking is required in holds, which reduces cargo space
- forced air is blown through the hold, which may dry the cargo.
- it cannot run while loading is in progress due to cold air blast inside the holds.

Hold Preparation

Reefer cargoes, being perishable in nature, require a great deal of care before loading and during carriage. Since most reefer cargoes are for human consumption, cleanliness of the compartments is of utmost importance.

The crew's understanding of the reefer plant is also important and pre-cooling checks should be carried out prior to operating the plant. The insulation must be checked for possible damage, the fans tested and the air ducting, sounding and scupper pipes must be checked. The actual process of cleaning the holds depends on the cargo to be loaded. Often, the shipper specifies the standard of cleanliness required and may appoint a surveyor for a pre-load inspection. The cleaning products to be used are sometimes prescribed by the shipping line and alternative products must not be used without permission.

In some cases, a dry wipe and sweep may suffice, although often a more thorough cleaning is required. This may be in case of changing cargoes from meat to fish or from frozen to chilled. In such cases, the holds are washed down and wiped clean with cloths drenched in a disinfectant solution. The bilges are thoroughly cleaned and disinfected. The gratings are also removed and washed with a disinfectant solution. Bloodstains or other deposits must be scraped out as this can be a fertile breeding ground for bacteria. The hold may be sprayed using antiseptic spray to prevent the growth of bacteria and moulds.

Residual odours from previous cargoes must also be removed or cargoes will be spoiled by *taint*[2]. On dedicated reefer ships, brine is pumped into the drainage pipes on tween decks. These pipes have an 'S' bend and the brine remains standing in it. Since brine has a low freezing point, it will not freeze or allow odours to pass through the pipe but will still allow any drip water to flow to the bilges.

Any dunnage is inspected and unusable dunnage is disposed of. Air filled dunnage is increasingly used on modern ships because of environmental concerns about the disposal of untreated wood. If any hooks and chains are used in the transportation process, they may need to be sterilised.

Once the hold is cleaned and dry, the *pre-cooling* process can begin. This usually takes about 48 hours. Any wooden dunnage to be used must be pre-cooled at the same time.

All temperatures must be recorded in the *temperature log*. Once the hold is at the right temperature, the surveyor usually inspects it and provides a survey report based on his findings. If the shipper accepts this, the loading process can begin.

Stowage and Cargo Care
Prior to loading the cargo, it should be inspected for damage. The shipowner is not usually liable for any damage claims registered prior to loading.

Once the cargo is loaded on board then proper care must be exercised in the stowage process. 'Live' cargoes need a supply of fresh air to survive and the stowage should be carefully monitored in order to avoid *shortcycling*.

Shortcycling is when a section of the cargo does not receive fresh air due to being stowed too close together. Since airflow chooses the path of least resistance, it passes around rather than through the cargo. Dunnage can be used to prevent this from happening. Frozen cargoes usually require no ventilation and this should be checked. The carriage temperature requirements must be carefully noted and, in particular, the units must be checked. Although degrees Celsius are the international standard, in the USA degrees Fahrenheit are still commonly used. As zero°C is a common chilled goods temperature and zero°F is a common frozen goods temperature, great care

---

[2] *Cargoes such as cheese are sensitive to taint and must be separated from strong smelling cargoes or cleaning material.*

is needed to avoid possible confusion of units.

Once the cargo is properly stowed, the temperatures must be carefully monitored during the voyage. Accurate records must be maintained to avoid future cargo damage claims.

References:
"Refrigeration at Sea", (1978) Second Edition, Munton R & Stott JR, Applied Science Publishers, London
"Marine Refrigeration Manual" Capt. A.W.C Alders; 1987 Rotterdam Marine Chartering Agents

KEY POINTS

♦ **Bulk cargoes transported by sea have inherent hazards**

♦ **knowledge of the hazards is important in order to safely transport these cargoes.**

Discharging Coal Cargo

The main hazards of bulk cargoes are:

- Liquefaction
- cargo shift
- structural damage due to improper distribution
- chemical hazards
- other health hazards.

Liquefaction

Excessive moisture content in certain cargoes may cause them to liquefy due to the vibration caused by the ship's movement. This can cause a *flow state* to develop, resulting in a loss of stability and structural damage due to impact. Compaction and vibration may cause a viscous fluid state to develop and the cargo may flow to one side of the ship with a roll one way but not completely return with a roll the other way. Therefore, the ship may progressively reach a dangerous heel and capsize.

Appendix A of the Bulk Cargo (BC) Code provides a list of such cargoes. At moisture content above that of the cargo's *transportable moisture limit (TML),* shift of cargo may occur as a result of liquefaction. For certain cargoes, this can also occur below TML due to rapid *moisture migration*[1]. Such cargoes should be trimmed level and loaded as deep as is possible.

This moisture content in certain cargoes may be as a result of its properties or because of the fact that many bulk cargoes are stowed in the open, without shelter. Cargoes affected include fine granular cargoes, such as fine coal and concentrates.

Precautions as provided in the *BC Code*

- Ships, other than specially constructed ships, should only carry these cargoes if the moisture content does not exceed the TML, as defined in the Code
- cargoes containing liquids should not be stowed in the same cargo space above or adjacent to consignments of cargoes with a tendency to liquefaction
- adequate precautions must be taken to prevent the entry of water into the holds
- while at sea, water should not be used as a cooling medium for such cargoes
- specially fitted cargo ships:
  - if the moisture content exceeds the TML then such materials may be carried in cargo ships designed with portable divisions that contain any shift of cargo. Such divisions should be of sufficient strength and not constructed of wood

- approval from the administration is required prior to carrying such material in these ships
- specially constructed cargo ships
  - ships may be specially constructed to carry the above cargoes and will be approved to do so by their respective administrations.

Section 8 of the BC Code details test procedures for verifying the moisture content of cargoes. A simple shipboard test procedure as detailed in the BC Code is as follows:

"Half fill a cylindrical can (0.5 to 1 ℓ) with a sample of the material. Strike a hard surface with the can sharply from a height of about 0.2 metres, repeating about 25 times at one or two second intervals. Examine the surface for free moisture or fluid conditions. If apparent then arrangements should be made to have additional laboratory tests conducted before the material is accepted for shipment".

Prior to loading such cargoes, the Master should insist on a certificate, from the shipper or the terminal, detailing the moisture content of a representative sample of the substance. The certificate will form a part of the information exchange between the ship and terminal, as required by the *BLU Code,* and for UK vessels or vessels at ports in the UK, the *SLU Code.*

Risk of cargo shift
Cargo may shift on passage if non-cohesive cargo is stowed incorrectly.

---

[1] *The movement of moisture from within the substance to the surface caused mainly by vibration*

The risk of cargoes shifting is determined by their *angle of repose*.

An angle of repose is defined as:

"...the maximum slope angle of non-cohesive, ie free flowing, granular material. It is the angle between the horizontal plane and the cone of such material when at rest on a plane surface".

Angles of repose

Cargoes with an angle of repose of less than 35° are considered to be in danger of shifting. Cargoes with an angle of repose higher than 35° have less likelihood of shifting due to the cohesive nature of such cargoes. In other words, the *lesser* the angle of repose, the *higher* the danger of a cargo shift.

A shipboard test to determine the angle of repose of a granular substance is detailed in the BC Code Appendix D.

To prevent a shift of cargo, in general, all bulk cargoes should be trimmed level and to the boundaries of the holds as far as is possible. At the very least, all cargoes must be trimmed to well below the cargo's angle of repose. Cargoes with a very low angle of repose (below 30°) need special precautions and for such cargoes, which will be similar in

nature to grain, the *International Grain Code* must be consulted and followed.[2]

Structural hazards due to improper distribution

In recent years, due to increasing numbers of incidents involving casualties that are caused by structural damage, attention has focused on this aspect of bulk carriers. SOLAS Chapter XII '*Additional Safety Measures for Bulk Carriers*' addresses these concerns. In the UK, *SI 2151 of 2004* makes the fitting of water level detectors in holds, ballast tanks and void spaces and drainage and pumping systems compulsory. This is in line with SOLAS Chapter XII 2004 amendments.

Structural damage to bulk carriers can occur because of excessive loading rates of high density cargo or due to such cargo being dropped into the hold from a height. The BLU Code addresses these concerns and forms a part of the ship-shore safety checklist on bulk carriers.

Structural damage to bulk carriers can also occur through improper weight distribution of the cargo. This can be caused by excessive concentration of weight in a particular area of the vessel. *Alternate hold loading* can cause excessive shearing forces and resultant stresses in the ship's structure, as shown by the following diagram.

This sort of loading should only be allowed if the alternate holds are specially strengthened. The advantage of loading alternate holds is that it raises the centre of gravity and eases racking stresses.

Block hold loading, where cargo is stowed in blocks of two or more adjoining holds, should only be adopted when either such a loading condition is described in the approved loading manual or approved local loading criteria defines the maximum weight limit in each hold or block of holds as a function of the ship's mean draught.

Uneven distribution of the cargo throughout the vessel's length can cause excessive shearing forces and bending moments. Prior to loading, a cargo plan must be made and due allowance made for the rates of ballast discharge. The BLU Code details a pro forma loading plan.[3] A *Loadicator* is normally used to ensure that the stresses on the ship do not exceed set limits.

Improper distribution of weight can lead to excessive stability, especially with high-density cargoes such as iron ore. This can result in *raking stresses* on the ship's structure. The resulting heavy rolling, caused by excessive stability, can also cause a shift of cargo.

Chemical and other health hazards

Some bulk cargoes, such as sulphur, are hazardous to human health because of their toxic or corrosive nature. These cargoes are listed in Appendix B of the BC Code[4]. Some of these materials are classified as dangerous goods in the International Maritime Dangerous Goods Code (IMDG Code), others are materials that may cause hazard when transported in bulk. Such material must be carefully segregated from other materials.

Hazards from such cargoes include the possibility of a flammable atmosphere being created, for example methane emission in coal, toxicity, corrosive properties, irritant dust, or oxygen depletion.

Prior to loading cargoes that have chemical hazards, it is important that adequate information is obtained from the shipper. This information should list all known chemical hazards of the cargo and the precautions to be taken on board. Such precautions will include, among other things, proper PPE to be worn, atmosphere tests, no smoking regulations enforced, proper cargo venting precautions, protecting machinery from cargo dust, wearing of dust masks, and securing all openings to the accommodation. *SI 336 (Carriage of Cargoes) 1999* makes it mandatory on UK registered vessels to carry atmosphere-monitoring equipment onboard, together with training and instructions for its use.

---

[3] *See Chapter 1.20*
[4] *See Chapter 1.19*

1.19 BC Code - Code of Safe Practice for Solid Bulk Cargoes

The BC Code provides guidance on the standards to be applied in the safe stowage and shipment of solid bulk cargoes *excluding* grain.

The Code of Safe Practice for Solid Bulk Cargoes includes general advice on the procedures to be practised or followed whenever bulk cargoes are shipped, a description of the hazards associated with certain materials, lists of typical bulk materials and recommended test procedures to determine the various characteristics of solid bulk cargoes. The BC Code deals with three basic types of cargo:

- Those which may liquefy
- materials that possess chemical hazards
- materials that fall into neither of these categories but may still pose other dangers.

The Code highlights the dangers associated with the shipment of certain types of bulk cargo, gives guidance on various procedures that should be adopted, lists typical products that are shipped in bulk, provides advice on their properties and how they should

BC Code

Code of Safe Practice for Solid Bulk Cargoes

be handled and describes various test procedures that should be employed to determine the characteristic cargo properties.

Contents of the Code
Introduction: A list of hazards associated with the shipment of materials

- Structural damage due to improper distribution
- loss or reduction of stability during the voyage
  - due to cargo shift
  - due to liquefaction
- chemical reactions.

Section 1: Contains key definitions related to bulk cargoes including angle of repose, flow state, etc.[1]

Section 2: Deals with general precautions.

Cargo distribution:

- Guidance to prevent the structure from becoming overstressed
- for high-density materials, the maximum number of tonnes loaded in an cargo space should not exceed 0.9 LBD tonnes

  (L = length of hold, B = average breadth of hold, D = summer draught)

- if material is trimmed level then the maximum tonnes loaded in the lower hold can be increased by 20%
- for untrimmed or partially trimmed material, the corresponding height of material pile peak above the cargo space floor should not exceed

  1.1 × D × Stowage factor

- the Master to be provided with adequate information about the material to be shipped by the shipper, eg stowage factor, history of shifting, any particular problems and information to aid in stability calculations onboard.

Loading and unloading:

- Prepare cargo spaces prior to loading
- make sure bilge lines, sounding pipes, bilge fittings, etc are in order
- sound bilges after completion of loading
- protect sensitive navigation equipment and deck machinery from dust, shut down ventilation systems and put accommodation air-conditioning system on recirculation.

Section 3: Deals with the safety of the personnel and the ship.

- General requirements
- poisoning, corrosive and asphyxiation hazards
  - shipper should inform about any chemical hazards
  - the Master should take all necessary precautions, including those for oxygen depletion and toxic gases
  - precautions to be followed for entry into enclosed spaces
- health hazards due to dust
- flammable atmosphere caused by fine dust and flammable gases emitted by cargoes
- advice on ventilation
- precaution for grain in in-transit fumigation
  - should be as per the latest version of the '*Recommendation on the Safe Use of Pesticides in Ships*'.

Section 4: Provides an assessment of acceptability for safe shipment.

- The shipper should provide details about the material being shipped prior to shipment. These should include the following:
  - chemical hazards
  - flow moisture point

[1] *Refer to Chapter 1.18*

- stowage factor
- moisture content
- angle of repose
- the shipper will arrange tests to be carried out on the material and certificates of test should be obtained. As examples:
  - moisture content: certificates containing the TML should be accompanied by a statement stating that the moisture content is the average moisture content at the time of shipment
  - chemical hazards
- the Master should ensure that such certificates are handed over to him prior to shipment.

Section 5: Trimming Procedures
- To minimise the dangers of a cargo shift, the cargo should be trimmed reasonably level to the boundaries of the hold
- documented history of the cargo should be made available to provide an indication of the cargo behaviour in the past.

Section 6: Methods of determining the angle of repose.
Shipboard test to determine angle of repose.[2]

Section 7: Cargoes that may liquefy. Properties, characteristics and hazards of cargoes that may liquefy:
- Appendix A to the Code contains a list of such cargoes
- at moisture content above that of the TML, shift of cargo may occur as a result of liquefaction

- for certain cargoes, this can also occur below TML because of rapid moisture migration
- such cargoes should be trimmed level and loaded as deep as is possible
- compaction and vibration may cause a viscous fluid state to develop and the cargo may flow to one side of the ship with a roll one way, but not completely return with a roll the other way. Therefore, the ship may progressively reach a dangerous heel and capsize.

Precautions
- Ships, other than specially constructed ships, should only carry these cargoes if the moisture content does not exceed the TML, as defined in the Code
- should not be stowed in the same cargo space above or adjacent to consignments of such cargoes
- adequate precautions must be taken to prevent the entry of water into the holds
- while at sea, water should not be used as a cooling medium for such cargoes.

Specially fitted cargo ships
- If the moisture content exceeds the TML then such materials may be carried in cargo ships designed with portable divisions that contain any shift of cargo. The divisions should be of sufficient strength and not constructed of wood

- approval from the administration is required prior to carrying such material in these ships
- ships may be specially constructed to carry the cargoes and will be approved to do so by their Administration.

Section 8: Test procedures for cargoes that may liquefy.
Shipboard test to determine risk of liquefaction.[3]

Section 9: Materials possessing chemical hazards
These may be materials classified as dangerous goods as per the IMDG Code, or materials hazardous only in bulk (MHB). They are listed in Appendix B of the Code.

- The Master should obtain currently valid information about the physical and chemical properties of the cargoes to be transported
- approval from the concerned competent authorities should be obtained for the transport of hazardous materials not listed in Appendix B
- classification of materials possessing chemical hazards and intending to be shipped in bulk is in accordance with the IMDG Code
- materials hazardous only in bulk (MHB) are defined as "materials, when carried in bulk, possess sufficient hazards to require specific precautions". For example, materials liable to self-heat or reduce oxygen in the space
- stowage and segregation requirements

- the table lists the segregation of bulk materials possessing chemical hazards and dangerous goods that are carried in packaged form
- segregation between incompatible bulk materials possessing chemical hazards qualities is listed in the table.

Section 10: Transport of solid bulk wastes.
This section outlines the requirements for the transport of solid wastes in bulk.

- Wastes are defined as solid materials containing or contaminated with materials possessing chemical hazards and which are carried for dumping or incineration
- in addition to the documentation required for solid bulk material, a waste movement document should be carried for all trans-boundary movements of waste
- waste should be classified as per the chemical hazards it possesses and segregated according to the Code
- in the event of an incident involving these goods, which may constitute a danger for the ship or the environment, the competent authorities of the countries of origin and destination should be informed and their advice obtained.

Appendix A — List of bulk materials that may liquefy.
This lists materials that may liquefy if carried at moisture content in excess of the transportable moisture limit.

[3] Refer to Chapter 1.18

Appendix B — List of bulk material possessing chemical hazards
This lists materials known to have chemical hazards that may give rise to a dangerous situation onboard.

The materials are listed along with their UN numbers, IMO class, EmS no., properties, observations, stowage and segregation requirements and any other special requirements.

Some of the classified materials listed also appear in the International Maritime Dangerous Goods (IMDG) Code when carried in packaged form, but others become hazardous only when they are carried in bulk, for example because they might reduce the oxygen content of a cargo space or are prone to self-heating. Examples are woodchips and coal.

Appendix B

SILICOMANGANESE*

(With known hazard profile or known to evolve gases)
With a silicon content of 25% or more

BC No.	IMO class	MFAG table no.	Approximate Stowage Factor (m³/t)	EmS No.
060	MHB	601,605	0.18 to 0.26	B2

Properties
In contact with water, alkalis or acids may evolve hydrogen, a flammable gas; may also produce phosphine and arsine, which are highly toxic gases.

Observations
Prior to loading, a certificate should be provided by the manufacturer or shipper stating that, after manufacture, the material was stored under cover, but exposed to the open air for not less than three days prior to shipment.

Segregation and stowage requirements
Segregation as required for class 4.3 materials.
'Separated from' foodstuffs and all class 8 liquids.
Only to be loaded under dry weather conditions.
Keep dry.
To be stowed in a mechanically ventilated space.

Special requirements
Ventilation should be such that any escaping gases cannot reach living quarters on or under deck.

Appendix C — Lists bulk materials that are neither liable to liquefy or possess chemical hazards.

The materials are listed in a tabular form with their approximate angle of repose, stowage factor and properties, observations and special requirements.

Appendix D — Lists the laboratory test procedures, associated apparatus and standards.

This also lists a shipboard test method to determine the angle of repose using a protractor.

Appendix E — Lists the Emergency Schedules (EmS) for materials possessing chemical hazards that are listed in Appendix B.

This section also advises the carriage of additional protective clothing, Breathing Apparatus (BA) sets, and spray jets for dealing with emergencies involving bulk solids.

The emergency action described in the Code is mainly for use at sea.

In general, the best action is to batten down the hold and exclude all air from the cargo space. There are notable exceptions to this rule, eg ammonium nitrate fertilisers.

EMERGENCY SCHEDULE B2

ALUMINIUM FERROSILICON POWDER (UN No. 1395)
ALUMINIUM SILICON POWDER, UNCOATED (UN No. 1398)
FERROPHOSPHORUS (BC No. 020)
FERRO SILICON (UN No. 1408) (BC No. 022)
SILICOMANGANESE (BC No. 060)

Special emergency equipment to be carried

Self-contained breathing apparatus

EMERGENCY PROCEDURES

Wear self-contained breathing apparatus.

EMERGENCY ACTION IN A FIRE SITUATION

Batten down and use CO_2 if available, **Do not use water.**

Medical first aid

UN/BC no.	Material	MFAG table no.
1395	ALUMINIUM FERROSILICON	601 and 605
1398	ALUMINIUM SILICON	NONE
BC 020	FERROPHOSPHORUS	601 and 605
1408, BC 022	FERRO SILICON	601 and 605
BC 060	SILICOMANGANESE	NONE

Remarks: Materials are virtually non-combustible when dry

The medical first aid advice refers to the *Medical First Aid Guide for Use in Accidents Involving Dangerous Goods (MFAG)*.

Appendix F — Lists recommendations for entering enclosed spaces onboard ships.

This lists precautions for the assessment of risk, permit to work systems, testing the atmosphere and precautions during entry. A sample permit to work checklist is attached.

This section also lists oxygen depleting cargoes and materials that may be carried in bulk.

Appendix G — Procedures for gas monitoring of coal cargoes.

This lists sampling, measurement and observation procedures for coal cargoes carried in bulk.

1.20 BLU Code

KEY POINTS

♦ IMO published the BLU Code in response to increasing losses of bulk carriers

♦ gives guidance to terminals and vessels for the safe loading and unloading of bulk carriers.

The *'Code of Practice for the Safe Loading and Unloading of Bulk Carriers'* *(BLU Code)* was written in response to continued losses of ships carrying solid bulk cargoes. This Code provides guidance to masters of bulk carriers, terminal operators and other parties concerned with the safe handling, loading and unloading of solid bulk cargoes.

For UK flag vessels and other vessels in UK waters, the contents of the Code are mandatory with effect from the 1st March 2004, vide the *"Merchant Shipping (Safe Loading and Unloading of Bulk Carriers) Regulations 2003"*.

BLU Code

Discharging Grain Cargo

Structure of the BLU Code

Definitions of terms
Includes

- Air draught
- combination carrier
- conveyer system
- trimming.

Suitability of ships and terminals
Ships are required to carry:

- Valid certification
- stability and loading booklets
- stress calculators and be suitable for the intended cargo.

Terminals to have:

- Equipment certification
- calibrated weighing equipment
- knowledge of the hazards of bulk cargoes
- trained and rested personnel and only accept ships that can safely berth alongside their installation.

Procedures between ship and terminal prior to arrival

- Information exchange
- loading rates
- cargo handling plan
- air draught, draught
- cargo properties
- limitations on loading procedures and cargo details
- trimming procedures.

Procedures for cargo loading

- Completion of safety checklist
- loading rates
- ballast rates

- times for checking draught
- stress limitations for ship's hull
- communication procedures
- accurate weight meters to within 1% of the intended accuracy
- emergency procedures.

Cargo unloading and handling of ballast

- Avoid excessive stresses
- unloading rates
- inform terminal immediately in the event of damage to the ship
- ship kept upright
- communication arrangements.

On completion of unloading, the Master and the terminal representative should agree in writing that the ship has been unloaded in accordance with the agreed unloading plan, with the holds emptied and cleaned to the Master's requirements. Any detected damage suffered by the ship should be recorded.

Appendices
Recommended contents of terminal information books.
Format for loading/unloading plan, with examples.
Ship/Shore Safety Checklist and guidelines for completion.
Form for receiving cargo information containing items such as:

- Stowage factor
- angle of repose
- trimming procedures
- moisture content
- transportable moisture limit
- chemical properties
- additional certificates to be attached for moisture content.

KEY POINTS

♦ Coal is an inherently hazardous cargo carried commonly in bulk carriers

♦ MGN 60 and the BC Code draw attention to the hazards of coal carriage and the precautions to be taken for the safe transport of coal cargoes.

'Trade Daring' Structural Failure

The different types of coal that may be carried by sea include:

Anthracite: Coal of a high rank which has a high carbon and low volatile matter content

Steam coal: Bituminous coal normally used as fuel for power plants

Duff: Small, ungraded coal with a nominal upper size, usually below 10 mm

Sized coal: Graded coal containing a minimum amount of fines, suitable for domestic or industrial use

Washed coal: Coal from which impurities have been reduced in order to improve its quality

Bunkering coal: The supply of coal to bunkers for the bunkering of ships.

Hazards of coal cargoes include:

1. They may emit flammable gases

    Coal cargoes may emit methane gas, which is flammable and lighter than air. The flammable range of methane is within the limits 5-16%, and this mixture can ignite on the introduction of a source of ignition. Accumulations of this gas may take place between the hatch coamings and the top of the cargo.

Methane may also leak into adjacent places and adjoining tanks. To prevent this, MGN 60 and the BC Code recommend surface ventilating the hold for 24 hours after departure from the loading port. If the methane concentration is found to be acceptably low at the end of this period, the ventilation should be stopped. However, if the concentration of methane as measured is over 20% of the LEL (Lower Explosive Limit), adequate surface ventilation is to be maintained to reduce the concentration.

Smoking and naked flames should not be allowed within the vicinity of any coal cargoes and a hot work permit system must be in place.

2. It has a tendency to self-heat

Some coals have a tendency to self-heat and if this is the case the shipper should be able to inform you prior to loading. Any self-heating is indicated by an increasing concentration of carbon monoxide in the hold. To minimise the tendency of the coal to self-heat, MGN 60 recommends that the hatches are kept closed and surface ventilation is limited to the absolute minimum to remove any accumulated methane.

The BC Code also recommends that the cargo is trimmed level to avoid the formation of any gas pockets and to prevent air from entering the body of the coal, which may cause self-heating. Carbon monoxide may be produced as a by-product of combustion. This is a toxic, odourless and flammable gas. The ship should also have available adequate instruments to detect and measure concentrations of harmful gases (methane, oxygen and carbon monoxide) within the hold. There should also be adequate sampling points sited as per Appendix G of the BC Code.

Carbon monoxide and, where necessary, temperature levels, must be monitored at regular intervals and logged. If, at the time of loading, when the hatches are open, the temperature of the coal exceeds 55°C, expert advice should be obtained prior to loading.

If the carbon monoxide level is increasing steadily, self-heating may be developing. The cargo space should be completely closed down and all ventilation ceased. The Master should seek expert advice immediately. Water should not be used for cooling the material or fighting coal cargo fires at sea, but it may be used for cooling the boundaries of the cargo space.

3. Oxidation

Coal may be subject to oxidation, which can cause the depletion of oxygen from the holds. This is hazardous if proper precaution is not taken while entering spaces that may be lacking in oxygen. There should be adequate procedures in place for enclosed space entry and readings for oxygen must be taken prior to entry.

4. Reaction with water

    Some coals are liable to react with water and produce acids that can cause corrosion. Flammable and toxic gases, including hydrogen, may be produced. Hydrogen is a colourless and odourless gas that is highly flammable and lighter than air.

    Monitoring of bilge water for acidity levels using *Ph* indicator strips will give an indication of this happening and adequate precautions should then be taken to prevent a hazard from developing.

5. Liquefaction hazards

    If fine coals with a size of less than 7 mm are carried, there is a risk of the coal liquefying if the moisture content exceeds the *transportable moisture limit (TML)*. The Master should ensure that the moisture content does not exceed the TML and, if necessary, the onboard test as recommended in the BC Code must be carried out to check the actual moisture content.

    The BC Code recommends the following precautions to be taken prior to loading, during carriage and discharge of all coal cargoes.

    Prior to loading, the shipper or his appointed agent should provide, in writing to the Master, the characteristics of the cargo and the recommended safe handling procedures for loading and transport of the cargo. As a minimum, the cargo's contract specifications for moisture content, sulphur content and size should be stated. It is important to state whether the cargo may be liable to emit methane or self-heat. The Master should be satisfied that he has received such information prior to accepting the cargo. If the shipper has advised that the cargo is liable to emit methane or self-heat, the Master should take the appropriate steps to prevent a hazard from developing.

Before and during loading, and while the material remains onboard, the master should ensure the following:

- All cargo spaces and bilge wells should be clean and dry

- any residue of waste material or previous cargo should be removed, including removable cargo battens, before loading

- all electrical cables and components situated in cargo spaces and adjacent spaces should be free from defects. Such cables and electrical components should either be safe for use in an explosive atmosphere or they should be positively isolated

- the ship should be suitably fitted and carry on board appropriate calibrated instruments for measuring concentrations of methane, oxygen and carbon monoxide and the pH value of cargo hold bilge samples. This should be possible without entering the space

- means should be provided for measuring the temperature of the cargo in the range 0°C to 100°C. Such arrangements should enable the temperature of the coal to be measured while being loaded and during the voyage without requiring entry into the cargo space

- the ship should carry on board the self-contained breathing apparatus required by SOLAS Regulation II/2 - 17. No smoking regulations must be imposed and warning signs and placards must be displayed

- the Master should ensure that the coal cargo is not stowed adjacent to hot areas.

Prior to departure, the Master should be satisfied that the surface of the material has been trimmed reasonably level to the boundaries of the cargo space to avoid the formation of gas pockets and to prevent air from permeating the body of the coal. Casings leading into the cargo space should be adequately sealed. The shipper must ensure that the loading terminal cooperates with the ship during the loading process.

If the behaviour of the cargo during the voyage differs from that specified in the cargo declaration, the Master should report such differences to the shipper. Such reports will enable the shipper to maintain records on the behaviour of the coal cargoes, so that in future the information provided to the Master can be reviewed in the light of prior experience.

KEY POINTS

♦ Carriage of grain in bulk is hazardous due to the possibility of shift of cargo because of the low 'angle of repose' of grain

♦ the *International Code for the Safe Carriage of Grain in Bulk* details the principles and procedures for the safe carriage of grain.

Discharging Grain using a Grab

Compliance with the *International Grain Code* is a requirement under SOLAS. For UK ships and foreign flag ships in UK waters, this is enforced by SI 336 (Carriage of Cargoes Regulations).

The *International Code for the Safe Carriage of Grain in Bulk* normally applies to all ships, regardless of size, engaged in the transport of bulk grain. However, some ships may be exempted from complying with the Code by their flag state due to the sheltered nature of their trade or the specific conditions of the voyage.

Part A contains special requirements and gives guidance on the stowage of grain and the use of grain fittings.

Part B deals with the calculation of heeling moments and general assumptions.

Part C of the revised SOLAS Chapter VI, Regulation 9, stipulates the requirements for cargo ships carrying grain. This states that a cargo ship carrying grain shall comply with the requirements of the International Grain Code and hold a document of authorisation as required by that Code. In Regulation 9.2, a ship without a document of authorisation shall not load grain until the Master satisfies the Contracting Governments of the port of loading that the ship complies with the requirements of the Code.

According to the Code, the term *grain* covers the following cargoes:

> *"...wheat, maize (corn), oats, rye, barley, rice, pulses, seeds and processed forms thereof, whose behaviour is similar to grain in its natural state".*

To prove compliance with the Code, a *Document of Authorisation* is issued for every ship that satisfies the conditions. This document should accompany or be incorporated into a ship specific *grain loading manual*. Both these documents are issued by or approved on behalf of that ship's flag state administration. A ship without a Document of Authorisation may be granted an *exemption,* provided the Master can demonstrate compliance with the terms of the Code.

Contents of the grain loading manual:

- Ship's particulars
- light ship displacement
- table of liquid free surface corrections
- capacities and centres of gravity
- curve or table of angle of flooding where less than 40°
- curves or tables of hydrostatic properties, suitable for a range of operating draughts
- approved curves or tables of volumes, vertical centres of volumes and assumed volumetric heeling moments for every compartment
- approved tables or curves of maximum permissible heeling moments for varying displacements and varying vertical centres of gravity
- loading instructions
- a worked example, for the guidance of the Master
- loaded departure and arrival conditions for 3 representative stowage factors.

Stability Requirements

- Vessels should be able to demonstrate by calculations that at all times during the intended voyage the ship will have sufficient intact stability to provide adequate residual dynamic stability after taking into account the adverse heeling effect caused by an assumed shift of grain
- the vessel should demonstrate by calculations that the maximum list will not be greater than 12° after experiencing
  - a shift of cargo of 15° in every full hold
  - a shift of cargo of 25° in any partly filled compartment
- net residual area between heeling arm curve and righting arm curve up to 40° (or angle of flooding if

- less than 40°) to be not less than 0.075 metre-radians
- initial metacentric height after free surface correction not to be less than 0.3 metres
- as many compartments full as possible
- cargo to be trimmed level.

Optional stability requirements for ships without a Document of Authorisation carrying partial cargoes of bulk grain:

The vessel may load grain if all the following conditions are met:
- The total weight of grain does not exceed one-third of the ship's deadweight
- filled compartments, trimmed and fitted with centre line divisions extending, full length and to a maximum depth of 2.4 m *or* be saucered (except in case of linseed or other such seeds)
- free grain surfaces in partially filled compartments to be trimmed level and secured in accordance with the Code
- must use GM 0.30 metres or as given by the formula in the Code (Section A 9.1.5), whichever is greater
- the Master must demonstrate to the administration that the ship, when loaded, will satisfy the requirements of this section of the Code.

Securing methods
To prevent a shift of cargo causing a heel beyond the permitted limits, the Code specifies methods of securing in full and partially full compartments.

In full compartments:
- Longitudinal shifting boards from the deckhead extending below the surface of the cargo
- for the purpose of reducing the heeling moment, a saucer may be used in place of a longitudinal division. The depth of the saucer, measured from the bottom of the saucer to the deck line, shall be as follows:
  - for ships with a moulded breadth of up to 9.1 m not less than 1.2 m, between 18.3 m or more, not less than 1.8 m and others on interpolation
  - the top of the saucer shall be formed by the under deck structure in way of the hatchway. The saucer and the hatchway above shall be completely filled with bagged grain or other suitable cargo laid down on a separation cloth and stowed tightly against the adjacent structure.

Bundling: As an alternative to filling the saucer with bagged grain, a bundle of bulk grain may be used provided that the dimensions and the securing means are as given in the Code.

Partly filled compartments:
- Overstowing the levelled off surface of the bulk grain with bagged grain or top of a separation cloth or a platform
- strapping or lashing two solid floors of lumber over the slightly crowned surface of the grain after covering with burlap or tarpaulin
- securing with a wire mesh, retained by wooden planks in place of the lumber pieces.

Saucer Secured by 'Bunding of Bulk'

Beam space may be filled with bulk grain or general cargo

*Minimum depth

Bulk grain

Dunnage

Lashings

'Liner' (of approved material)

Bulk grain

* Minimum depth of saucer in a 'filled compartment'

Vessels with a moulded breadth up to 9.1 m　　　= 1.2 m
Vessels with a moulded breadth 18.3 m or more　= 1.8 m
(Interpolate for breadths betweem 9.1 m and 18.3 m)

'Plan View' of Securing a Partly Filled Compartment

32 mm Turnbuckle

Bearer board

Longitudinal floor

2.4 m

Athwartships floor

Steel wire

Nailed

Tarpaulin

Grain

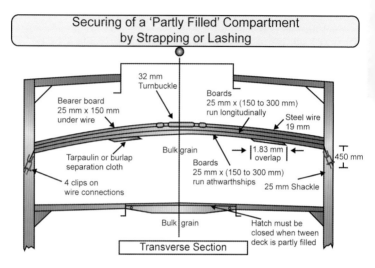

Securing of a 'Partly Filled' Compartment by Strapping or Lashing

32 mm Turnbuckle

Bearer board 25 mm x 150 mm under wire

Boards 25 mm x (150 to 300 mm) run longitudinally

Steel wire 19 mm

Tarpaulin or burlap separation cloth

Bulk grain

Boards 25 mm x (150 to 300 mm) run athwartships

1.83 mm overlap

450 mm

25 mm Shackle

4 clips on wire connections

Bulk grain

Hatch must be closed when tween deck is partly filled

Transverse Section

All lashings in partly filled compartments must be inspected regularly and tightened as necessary.

Prior to loading a cargo of grain, all holds must be thoroughly washed, dried and all residues of previous cargoes removed. Surveyors, appointed by shippers' prior to loading the cargo, may inspect the hold. Spaces should be closely inspected for insect infestation and fumigated if required. Any fumigation should be carried out in accordance with the IMO *'Recommendations on the Safe Use of Pesticides in Ships'* and MGN 284 – *'Recommendations for Ships Carrying Fumigated Bulk Cargoes'*.

1.23 Carriage of Dangerous Goods

Dangerous Goods Ready to be Loaded

ere are comprehensive and specific quirements for the transport of ngerous goods by sea. The purpose these requirements is to effectively otect the lives of seafarers, the fety of vessels and the maritime vironment.

ngerous Goods are divided into 9 sses based on their associated ks when transported by land, sea air. This classification is based on recommendations that were made 957.

The various classes are:

Class 1   Explosives

Class 2   Gases

Class 3   Flammable liquids

Class 4   Flammable solids
          Substances liable to
          spontaneous combustion
          Substances, which in contact
          with water, emit flammable
          gas

Class 5   Oxidising substances and
          organic peroxides

Class 6	Toxic and infectious substances
Class 7	Radioactive material
Class 8	Corrosive substances
Class 9	Miscellaneous dangerous substances.

Documentation required prior loading

The regulations governing the carriage of dangerous goods by sea casts a responsibility on the *shipper* of the goods to provide a *Dangerous Goods Declaration*[1]. This should include the following details:

a. The Proper Shipping Name of the material carried
   This is not the trade name but can be the technical name, as long as it accurately describes the goods.

b. The UN Number
   This is a 4 digit unique number allocated to all dangerous goods assigned by the United Nations committee of experts (UN List).

c. Hazard class
   From 1 to 9 as elaborated above.

d. Packing Group (when assigned)
   Dangerous substances of Classes 3, 4, 5.1, 6.1 and 8 have been assigned to one of three categories (Packaging Groups), according to the degree of danger they present:

   • Great danger - Packaging Group I (PGI)

   • medium danger - Packaging Group II (PGII)

   • minor danger - Packaging Group III (PGIII)

The greater the degree of danger, the more stringent the packaging requirement will be. For other classes, packaging groups may be assigned depending on the degree of severity of any leakage of the substance.

For the Sequence of the Information, two options are allowed:

a, b, c, d OR

b, c, a, d

Examples

"UN1098 ALLYL ALCOHOL, 6.1 (3), I"
"ALLYL ALCOHOL, 6.1 (3), UN1098, I"

e. Subsidiary Risk
   This is an additional risk that may be present in certain goods. For example, a corrosive substance may also be flammable.

f. Marine Pollutant
   This classification is included for any substance so classified as per Annex 3 of MARPOL.

g. Number of Packages
   Total number of packages to be transported as a unit.

h. Total Quantities
   The total volume or mass (in kilograms) is stated for each item of dangerous goods bearing a different Proper Shipping Name. For Class 1 goods, the quantity shall be the net explosive mass.

   If the dangerous goods are transported according to the exceptions for dangerous goods

[1] Also called a Dangerous Goods Note

packed in limited quantities,[2] then the words 'Limited Quantities' shall be included.

i. Flashpoint
If applicable, for liquid dangerous substances the flashpoint shall be included.

j. Any other information required by the IMDG Code or local regulations.

This will include additional information such as the 24 hour emergency contact number required for shipments to the US and additional certificates such as a weathering certificate, etc.

k. Container/Vehicle Packing Certificate
When dangerous goods are packed or loaded into any container or vehicle, those responsible for packing the container or vehicle shall provide a 'container/vehicle packing certificate' specifying the container/vehicle identification number and certifying that the operation is carried out in accordance with the following conditions:

- The container is clean and dry and fit to receive the goods

- packaging and labelling is carried out as per the IMDG Code

- segregation within the container/vehicle is as per the IMDG Code

- container is marked and labelled as per the IMDG Code

- a DG note (on next page) has been received for each dangerous goods consignment loaded in the container/vehicle.

The container/vehicle packing certificate and declaration serves a separate function to the dangerous goods declaration, and different people very often sign the two. However, for the sake of convenience, the two declarations are often included in the same document.

Documentation required onboard the ship

Dangerous Goods Manifest
Each ship carrying dangerous goods and marine pollutants shall have onboard a special list or manifest, setting out the dangerous goods and marine pollutants onboard and their locations. Instead of the manifest, a detailed stowage plan, which identifies all dangerous goods by class and sets out their location, may be used.

The dangerous goods declaration is used as a basis for making up the manifest and shall contain at least the information from the DG declaration and, *in addition,* should contain the stowage position and the total quantity of the dangerous goods or marine pollutants. A copy of the manifest or stowage plan is made available before departure to the person designated by the port authority.

Emergency Response Information
Appropriate information shall be immediately available for use in emergency response to accidents and incidents involving dangerous goods in transport. The information may be

DANGEROUS GOODS NOTE

© SITPRO 1999

Exporter	**1 Customs reference/status** 2
BATHUNT (UK) PLC	3GB 214832591000-T63981
PO BOX 830	**Booking number 3** **Exporter's reference 4**
CROYDON	BN001251 T6-3981
SURREY	**Forwarder's reference 5**
CR9 9NZ	ARG 4367H

Consignee 6 | **6A DSHA Notification in accordance with DSHA regulations (as ammended) given by**

	Shipper	Cargo Agent	Transport operator	Shipping line
CASILLA BOX S.A.		X		
CASILLA DE CORRERO 6091				
BUENOS AIRES				
ARGENTINA				

Freight forwarder 7 | **International carrier 8**

FORREST FORWARD COMPANY | ORCHARD SHIPPING
VENTURA BUSINESS PARK |
STAFFORDSHIRE DE15 4ZY | For use of receiving authority only

Other UK transport details (e.g. ICD, terminal, vehicle bkg. ref, receiving date) 9

DELIVER TO CONTAINER BASE MANCHESTER BY 5/6/03

I hereby declare that the contents of this consignment are fully and accurately described below by proper shipping name, and are classified, packaged, marked and labelled/placarded and are in all respects in proper condition for transport according to the applicable international and national governmental regulations and in accordance with the provisions shown overleaf. The shipper must complete and sign box 17 **10A**

Vessel	**Port of loading 10**
ORCHARD EMPRESS	LIVERPOOL
Port of Discharge	**Destination 11**
BUENOS AIRES	

TO THE RECEIVING AUTHORITY: Please receive for shipment the goods described below subject to your published regulations and conditions (including those as to liability)

Shipping marks Number and kind of packages; description of goods SPECIFY Proper Shipping Name*. Hazard Class, UN No.Additional Information (if applicable) see overleaf For RID/ ADR/ CDG Road requirements see notes overleaf **12**		**Net weight (kg) 13** of goods	**Gross weight (kg) 14A** of goods	**Cube (m³) (kg) 14** of goods
CB 11821 BUENOS AIRES	1 PALLET CONTAINING 10X200L DRUMS ALLYL ALCOHOL	1,800	2,000	4.00
UN 1098 ALLYL ALCOHOL, 6.1(3), I				

* Proper Shipping Name - Trade names alone are unacceptable

CONTAINER/VEHICLE PACKING CERTIFICATE I hereby declare that the goods described above have been packed/ loaded into the container vehicle identified below in accordance with the provisions shown overleaf. THE DECLARATION MUST BE COMPLETED AND SIGNED FOR ALL CONTAINER/ VEHICLE LOADS BY THE PERSON RESPONSIBLE FOR PACKING/LOADING	Name of Company Name/ Status of Declarant Place and date Signature of Declarant	THIS BOX WOULD BE COMPLETED BY THE COMPANY RESPONSIBLE FOR LOADING THE CONTAINER	**Total gross weight** of goods 2,000	**Total cube of goods** 4.00

Container identification number/ vehicle registration number 16	**Seal number(s)**	**Container/ vehicle size and type 16A**	**Tare (kg) 16B**	**Total gross weight (including tare) (kg) 16C** 16D
STPU284152/5	238795	40' GENERAL STANDARD HEIGHT	2,500	4,500

HAULIER DETAILS	**DOCK/TERMINAL RECIEPT** RECEIVING AUTHORITY REMARKS	Name and telephone number of shipper preparing this note **17**
Haulier's name	Received the above number of packages/containers/trailers in apparent good order and condition unless stated hereon.	BATHUNT (UK) PLC 020 8000 0000
		Name/status of declarant A POTTS SHIPPING CLERK
Vehicle reg. no.		Place and date CROYDON 20/5/03
Drivers signature	Receiving authority signature and date	Signature of declarant APotts

630 Non-completion of any boxes is a subject for resolution by the contracting parties

Dangerous Goods Note Completion Guide Revised Edition - June 2004 (SITPRO © 1999 Design)

combined with the Dangerous Goods Manifest or stowage plan and must be immediately accessible in the event of an incident.

The manifest or stowage plan may contain references to the emergency schedules found in column 15 of the dangerous goods list. These will be used, in conjunction with the supplement to the IMDG Code, to decide on a plan of action for emergencies involving dangerous goods or marine pollutants. In place of the above, separate safety data sheets may be provided for each dangerous cargo or marine pollutant carried.

Document of Compliance

Ships of the following descriptions:

- passenger ships constructed on or after 1 September 1984
- all other ships of 500 tons or over constructed on or after 1 September 1984
- all other ships of under 500 tons constructed on or after 1 February 1992

that are intended, or that have cargo spaces intended for, the carriage of dangerous goods on international voyages, must carry a *Document of Compliance*. The document of compliance will certify that the ship complies with Regulation 54 of Chapter 2 to the International Convention for the Safety of Life at Sea 1974 (SOLAS 1974) and will be limited to 5 years from the date of issue.

The document of compliance is issued by the flag state after a survey. This document is usually in the form of a diagram showing all the spaces on board in which dangerous goods can be loaded. A table then sets out the *classes* of dangerous goods that the ship is allowed to carry and the spaces in which these classes can be carried. The document also states additional requirements that must be fulfilled prior to carrying the dangerous goods or marine pollutants. This may include additional fire fighting equipment or ventilation in holds required for certain classes of dangerous goods.[3]

Extracts from MGN 36 showing spaces and classes of dangerous goods/marine pollutants that can be loaded in those spaces are overleaf.

Marking and labelling

All packaged dangerous goods must be marked and labelled as per the provisions of the IMDG Code. The marking will include an indication of the hazard class and other details such as the subsidiary risks, elevated temperatures, marine pollutants etc. These markings are required on all four sides of the container and, if the container is bound for an offshore installation, also on the roof.

Marking schemes for limited quantities, as per amendment 31, require that the outside of the package is marked with a diamond and with the UN number in the centre (including

MGN 36 'Document of Compliance for Ships Carrying Dangerous Goods in Solid or Dry Bulk Form', MCA, UK.

MARINE SAFETY AGENCY

ANNEX

Document of Compliance

Special Requirements for Ships carrying Dangerous Goods

Issued in pursuance of the requirement of regulations II-2/41 & II-2/54.3 of the International Convention for Safety of Life at Sea, 1974, as amended, under the authority of the Government of the United Kingdom of Great Britain and Northern Ireland

Name of ship

Distinctive number or letters   O.N.

Port of registry

Ship type   eg. Ro Ro Cargo Ferry, Container Ship

IMO Number (if applicable)

THIS IS TO CERTIFY:

    1   that the construction and equipment (see note 2) of the above mentioned ship was found to comply with the requirements of regulation II-2/54 of the International Convention for the Safety of Life at Sea, 1974, as amended; and

    2.   that the ship is suitable for the carriage of those classes of dangerous goods as specified in the appended schedule 1, subject to any provisions in the International Maritime Dangerous Goods (IMDG) Code and the Code of Safe Practice for Solid Bulk Cargoes (BC Code) for individual substances also being complied with.

This document is valid until the   day of .

Issued at Southampton on the .... of

....
....
(Signature of authorized official issuing the certificate)

NOTE 1:   There are no special requirements in the above-mentioned regulation II-2/54 for the carriage of dangerous goods of classes 6.2 and 7, or for the carriage of dangerous goods in "Limited Quantities", as stated in Section 18 of the General Introduction to the IMDG Code.

NOTE 2:   Schedule 2 lists the special requirements for this ship to carry dangerous goods within the spaces identified in Schedule 1.

Safe Ships Clean Seas

An executive agency of
THE DEPARTMENT OF THE
ENVIRONMENT, TRANSPORT
AND THE REGIONS

3

Schedule 1

The ship is suitable for the carriage of those classes of dangerous goods as specified in the table below, subject to any provisions in the International Maritime Dangerous Goods (IMDG) Code and the Code of Safe Practice for Solid Bulk Cargoes (BC Code) for individual substances also being complied with.

Spaces indicated on the diagram
UNDER-DECK SPACES

ON DECK SPACES

P = Packaged Goods Permitted

A = Packaged & Bulk Permitted

X = Not Permitted

Class	Space		
	1	2	3
1.1 - 1.5			
1.4.S			
2.1			
2.2			
2.3			
3.1 + 3.2 (FP < 23°C c.c.)			
3.3 (FP 23°C to 61°C c.c.)			
4.1			
4.2			
4.3			
5.1			
5.2			
6.1 liquids			
6.1 liquids (FP < 23°C c.c.)			
6.1 liquids (FP 23°C to 61°C c.c.)			
6.1 solids			
8 liquids			
8 liquids (FP < 23°C c.c)			
8 liquids (FP 23°C to 61°C c.c)			
8 solids			
9			

NOTE: Cargoes in bulk may be listed individually by name and class

[A number of footnotes may be given here with references to spaces, classes or substances in the table]

4

---

the letters 'UN' in front of the number). If there is more than one type of dangerous goods in the package, the diamond must be large enough to contain the UN numbers for all of them. The package does not have to display the class labels required, the marine pollutant mark, or the shipping name of the material.

All labels must be affixed in a way that they will still be identifiable on packages that have survived at least three months immersion in the sea.

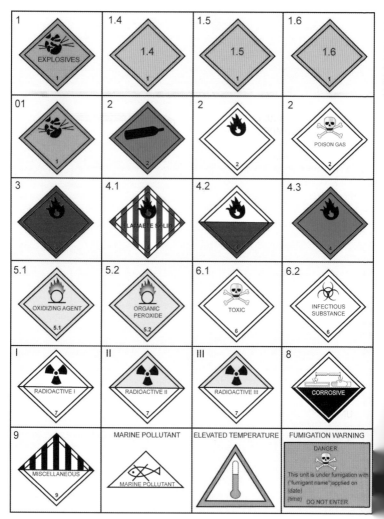

Dangerous Goods Labels

1.24 The International Maritime Dangerous Goods (IMDG) Code

The International Maritime Dangerous Goods (IMDG) Code is an international code for the shipment of dangerous goods by sea. It covers such matters as packing, container traffic and stowage, with emphasis on the segregation of incompatible substances.

It also lays down recommendations for packing, labelling, handling and for emergency response during incidents involving dangerous goods.

Amendments to SOLAS Chapter VII made the IMDG Code mandatory from the 1st January 2004[1] and the 32nd amendment, which entered into force on the 1st January 2005.

The major changes to the Code, as per amendment 32, are as follows:

- The inclusion of 90 additional UN numbers to cover items such as organo-metallic substances and substances that are toxic by inhalation

- a new chapter (1.4) regarding Security of Dangerous Goods in transit

- many new materials have been added to segregation groups, including the creation of a new category - Alkalis, containing 65

IMDG Code

UN numbers. Some acids are now termed 'Strong Acids'

- the Class 6.2 and Class 9 sections have been re-written. The transport schedules for Class 7 have been deleted

- extensive revisions to packing instructions, construction and testing of packaging provisions.

Amendment 31 to the Code makes it mandatory with effect from 1st January 2004

Structure of the IMDG Code

The two-volume Code is divided into seven parts:

Volume 1 – Parts 1, 2 and 4-7 of the Code

- General provisions
- definitions
- training
- classification
- packing and tank provisions
- consignment procedures
- construction and testing of packaging, IBCs, large packaging, portable tanks and road tank vehicles
- transport operations.

Volume 2

- The Dangerous Goods List presented in tabular format

- limited quantities exceptions
- the Index
- appendices.

The Supplement contains the following:

- Emergency involving dangerous goods
The supplement to the IMDG Code contains the emergency schedules for fire and spillage involving dangerous goods. Medical emergencies are covered in the Medical First Aid Guide (MFAG), and also in the supplement to the Code.

The Dangerous Goods List (Column 15) in Volume 2 contains references to the emergency schedules for spillage or fire for individual UN numbers. The first code is the fire schedule and the second code the spillage schedule

- fire schedules
There are 10 fire schedules, including a General Fire Schedule (F-A) and nine

Dangerous Goods Labelling

further schedules (F-B to F-J) dealing with particular groups of hazardous goods. Each schedule starts with a list of the UN numbers to which the schedule may be applicable. The schedule then starts with general comments on the danger of the cargo followed by sections dealing with cargoes on fire on deck, cargoes on fire under deck and cargoes exposed to fire. Most fire schedules then have a section dealing with special cases related to particular UN numbered cargoes. The notes on specific chemicals are generally more detailed than those in the last version

- spillage schedule
The 26 spillage schedules start with S-A, toxic substances, and end with S-Z, toxic explosives. As with the fire schedules, each starts with the list of applicable UN numbers. The sections generally correspond to the fire schedule ones but there is more differentiation between large and small spillages

- Medical First Aid Guide(MFAG)
In case of an emergency involving dangerous goods, the MFAG in the supplement to the IMDG Code should be referred to. This is arranged into three sections:

- A flowchart based emergency action and diagnosis

  Tables giving brief instructions for special circumstances

  Appendices giving comprehensive information, a list of medicines/drugs,

and a list of chemicals referred to in the table

- reporting procedures for accidents and incidents involving dangerous goods to be followed in conjunction with Flag State and Port State requirement, eg MAIB reports.

- guidelines for packing cargo transport units

- 'International Code for the Safe Carriage of Packaged Irradiated Nuclear Fuel' (INF Code)

- 'Recommendations for the Safe Use of Pesticides at Sea'.

Use of the Code
Prior to loading consignments of dangerous cargo or marine pollutant onboard, you must refer to the ship specific *Document of Compliance*[2] issued by the Flag State or a body authorised by the Flag State. This will specify the spaces available onboard for loading the dangerous goods and the additional equipment that may be required onboard. If the document of compliance allows you to load that substance then the next step is to get cargo related information from the cargo specific *dangerous goods declaration.*

Using the UN number from the dangerous goods declarations, refer to Volume 2 of the Code. The *Dangerous Goods List (DGL)* in Volume 2 of the Code will provide additional information about the cargo including its proper shipping name, subsidiary risk and properties.

Stowage

Each substance listed in the dangerous goods list will be allocated a stowage category. Class 1 goods will be allocated a numerical stowage category from 01 to 15, while for other classes the stowage requirements are categorised A, B, C, D or E.

The stowage requirements are found in Chapter 7.1 of Volume 1 of the IMDG Code. The stowage requirements range from 'on deck stowage only', 'on deck or under deck' or 'prohibited', depending on the category allocated to the substance and the number of passengers carried by the ship. The Dangerous Goods List (DGL) may also contain additional stowage requirements for individual goods.

Segregation

Once the stowage position has been allocated, the next step is to segregate the goods from other substances in the vicinity. The segregation requirements are dealt with in Chapter 7.2 of Volume 1 of the IMDG Code. The segregation requirements between dangerous goods carried on the same ship are laid out in a tabular format. The dangerous goods class is cross-referenced with the class of the other substances using the following table:

- Away from
- separated from
- separated by a complete compartment or hold from
- separated longitudinally by an intervening complete compartment or hold from.

Class		1.1 1.2 1.5	1.3 1.6	1.4	2.1	2.2	2.3	3	4.1	4.2	4.3	5.1	5.2	6.1	6.2	7	8	9
Explosives	1.1, 1.2, 1.5	*	*	*	4	2	2	4	4	4	4	4	4	2	4	2	4	x
Explosives	1.3, 1.6	*	*	*	4	2	2	4	3	3	4	4	4	2	4	2	2	x
Explosives	1.4	*	*	*	2	1	1	2	2	2	2	2	2	x	4	2	2	x
Flammable gases	2.1	4	4	2	x	x	x	2	1	2	x	2	2	x	4	2	1	x
Non-toxic, non-flammable gases	2.2	2	2	1	x	x	x	1	x	1	x	x	1	x	2	1	x	x
Toxic gases	2.3	2	2	1	x	x	x	2	x	2	x	x	2	x	2	1	x	x
Flammable liquids	3	4	4	2	2	1	2	x	x	2	1	2	2	x	3	2	x	x
Flammable solids**)	4.1	4	3	2	1	x	x	x	x	1	x	1	2	x	3	2	1	x
Substances liable to spontaneous combustion	4.2	4	3	2	2	1	2	2	1	x	1	2	2	1	3	2	1	x
Substances which, in contact with water, emit flammable gases	4.3	4	4	2	x	x	x	1	x	1	x	2	2	x	2	2	1	x
Oxidizing substances (agents)	5.1	4	4	2	2	x	x	2	1	2	2	x	2	1	3	1	2	x
Organic peroxides	5.2	4	4	2	2	1	2	2	2	2	2	2	x	1	3	2	2	x
Toxic substances	6.1	2	2	x	x	x	x	x	x	1	x	1	1	x	1	x	x	x
Infectious substances	6.2	4	4	4	4	2	2	3	3	3	2	3	3	1	x	3	3	x
Radioactive materials	7	2	2	2	2	1	1	2	2	2	2	1	2	x	3	x	2	x
Corrosives	8	4	2	2	1	x	x	x	1	1	1	2	2	x	3	2	x	x
Miscellaneous dangerous substances and articles	9	x	x	x	x	x	x	x	x	x	x	x	x	x	x	x	x	x

If the segregation requirements are given as an 'X' then the requirements, if any, between the two substances will be found in the 'properties and observations' column in the DGL (IMDG Volume 2).

Segregation between substances of Class 1 is found in the introduction to the Class 1 chapter in Volume 1 of the Code.

The next step is to refer the segregation requirements to the ship specific tables. There are separate tables for the following:

- Segregation of packages
- segregation of freight containers onboard container ships
- segregation of cargo transport units onboard Ro Ro ships

- segregation between bulk materials possessing chemical hazards and dangerous goods in packaged form.

For example, referring to the table that follows, for a Ro Ro vessel, the segregation requirement *away from* will mean the following:

Closed cargo transport units: no restrictions for their stowage in either the fore and aft direction or the athwartships direction.

Open transport units: a distance of at least three metres must be maintained between the units.

Table of segregation of cargo transport units on board Ro Ro ships:

SEGREGATION REQUIREMENT		HORIZONTAL					
		CLOSED VERSUS CLOSED		CLOSED VERSUS OPEN		OPEN VERSUS OPEN	
		ON DECK	UNDER DECK	ON DECK	UNDER DECK	ON DECK	UNDER DECK
AWAY FROM .1	FORE AND AFT	NO RESTRICTION	NO RESTRICTION	NO RESTRICTION	NO RESTRICTION	AT LEAST 3 METRES	AT LEAST 3 METRES
	ATWART-SHIPS	NO RESTRICTION	NO RESTRICTION	NO RESTRICTION	NO RESTRICTION	AT LEAST 3 METRES	AT LEAST 3 METRES
SEPARATED FROM 2	FORE AND AFT	AT LEAST 6 METRES	AT LEAST 6 METRES OR ONE BULKHEAD	AT LEAST 6 METRES	AT LEAST 6 METRES OR ONE BULKHEAD	AT LEAST 6 METRES	AT LEAST 12 METRES OR ONE BULKHEAD
	ATHWART-SHIPS	AT LEAST 3 METRES	AT LEAST 3 METRES OR ONE BULKHEAD	AT LEAST 3 METRES	AT LEAST 6 METRES OR ONE BULKHEAD	AT LEAST 6 METRES	AT LEAST 12 METRES OR ONE BULKHEAD
SEPARATED BY A COMPLETE COMPARTMENT OR HOLD FROM .3	FORE AND AFT	AT LEAST 12 METRES	AT LEAST 24 METRES + DECK	AT LEAST 24 METRES	AT LEAST 24 METRES + DECK	AT LEAST 36 METRES	TWO DECKS OR TWO BULKHEADS
	ATHWART-SHIPS	AT LEAST 12 METRES	AT LEAST 24 METRES + DECK	AT LEAST 24 METRES	AT LEAST 24 METRES + DECK	PROHIBITED	PROHIBITED
SEPARATED LONGITUDINALLY BY AN INTERVENING COMPLETE COMPARTMENT OR HOLD FROM .4	FORE AND AFT	AT LEAST 36 METRES	TWO BULKHEADS OR AT LEAST 36 METRES + TWO DECKS	AT LEAST 36 METRES	AT LEAST 48 METRES INCLUDING TWO BULKHEADS	AT LEAST 48 METRES	PROHIBITED
	ATHWART-SHIPS	PROHIBITED	PROHIBITED	PROHIBITED	PROHIBITED	PROHIBITED	PROHIBITED

NOTE: ALL BULKHEADS AND DECKS SHOULD BE RESISTANT TO FIRE AND LIQUID

Liquid and
Gas Cargoes

KEY POINTS

♦ **All personnel involved in the carriage of petroleum cargoes must be familiar with the hazards inherent in them**

♦ **knowledge of these hazards and the methods to reduce or eliminate them is critical for the safe transportation of petroleum product cargoes.**

The main hazards that are inherent in petroleum cargoes are:

• Flammability

• toxicity

• pollution.

Flammability

This is the primary hazard to be aware of during the carriage of petroleum cargoes. Petroleum vapour is easily ignited and burns with a visible flame. The level of flammability of a liquid is determined by its volatility and temperature, as these two factors determine the amount of vapour that will be released. It is always the vapour that ignites and burns and not the liquid itself.

This vapour forms the fuel side of the fire triangle depicted below.

Petroleum cargoes are generally divided into two broad categories that are based on their volatility and their *flashpoint* [1]:

• Non-volatile liquids are those with a flashpoint of 60°C or above, as determined by the closed cup method of testing

• Volatile liquids are those with a flashpoint below 60°C, as determined by the closed cup method.

The vapour given out by petroleum cargoes can only burn if it is mixed with air in certain proportions. If there is too much or too little vapour in the air mixture, the vapour will not burn. These limiting proportions, expressed as a percentage by volume of petroleum gas in air, are known as the lower and the upper flammable limits.

The *Lower Flammable Limit (LFL)* is that hydrocarbon concentration below which there is insufficient hydrocarbon gas to support and propagate combustion. The mixture is said to be too lean.

The *Upper Flammable Limit (UFL)* is that hydrocarbon concentration above

---

[1] Flashpoint is defined as the lowest temperature at which sufficient gases are evolved at the surface of the liquid to ignite when a naked flame is passed over it.

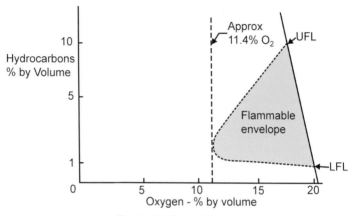

Flammable Range Diagram

which there is insufficient air to support combustion. The mixture in this case is said to be too rich.

For normal petroleum cargoes, the lower and upper flammable limits are usually between 1% and 10% by volume.

The *Flammable Range Diagram* above depicts the flammable limits and the *Flammable Envelope* is the range in which combustion can occur. To prevent ignition, it must be ensured that the atmosphere in the tank never passes through the flammable envelope.

Sources of ignition

The main sources of ignition on board a tanker are:

- Direct heat smoking, naked flames etc. Restricting the smoking areas on board a tanker to certain designated areas can stop this.

  All equipment used on deck must be intrinsically safe and certified for use in a flammable atmosphere.

  No naked flames must be allowed on deck and the carriage of lighters and matchboxes must be forbidden

- mechanical sparks – chipping, dropped tools etc. Opinion is divided as to whether sparks caused due to chipping, etc can cause ignition but, as far as possible, these activities must be restricted onboard a tanker. A risk assessment and permit to work system must be in use onboard. A tool belt must be worn if entering tanks to prevent sparks from falling metal tools

- electrical sparks – lightning, static discharge, electric arcing etc. All electrical equipment in use on decks and in gas dangerous areas must be intrinsically safe.

  All cargo and venting operations must be suspended if lightning is spotted in the vicinity.

Unauthorised use of cameras, radios, mobile phones, MP3 players, etc must be forbidden

- chemical energy – spontaneous combustion, auto–ignition, pyrophoric iron sulphide, metallic smears etc.

Spontaneous combustion can occur in the case of certain substances. For example, oily rags left in the open are at risk of igniting. Spontaneous combustion is the ignition of a material brought about by a heat producing chemical reaction within the material itself, without exposure to an external source of ignition.

Static electricity is the electricity produced when dissimilar materials with opposing charges are brought close together. Certain oils are capable of retaining a static charge and these are known as static accumulator oils. Particular care must be taken prior to introducing an unearthed object (for measuring ullage etc) into a tank containing static accumulator oils. The ullage tape must always be earthed to dissipate the charge prior to introducing it into the tank.

The flow of oil in pipelines and the dropping of oil on the tank top when loading may also cause static charges. The amount of water in the tank or in the oil also influences the static charge. Spraying water into the tanks during water washing can also give rise to an electrically charged mist. For this reason, initial loading rates must be slow and excess moisture must be prevented from entering the tank. To reduce the static generation properties of static accumulator oils, the shipper may add an anti-static additive.

Pyrophoric iron sulphide is iron sulphide capable of a rapid exothermic oxidation, causing incandescence and the ignition of any hydrocarbon/air mixtures when exposed to air. When any rust in the tank comes in contact with hydrogen sulphide, iron sulphide is formed. This reverts back to iron oxide in the presence of air and gives off heat and light. To prevent this, tanks must be kept inerted and rust free.

Metallic smears are caused when two dissimilar metals (eg aluminium and steel) are rubbed together, resulting in a metal deposit being formed. This can cause a chemical reaction, which gives off heat, between the metals.

Toxicity
Petroleum liquids and the vapour produced are inherently toxic and harmful to the personnel exposed to them. A number of indicators are used to measure the concentrations of toxic vapours and the main unit of measurement is the *Threshold Limit Value (TLV)*.

TLV is the average concentration of a substance to which workers may be exposed for a set time period. The values are expressed as parts per million (ppm) by volume of gas in air. It is more closely defined as follows:

TLV-TWA (Time Weighted Average). This is the average concentration of a substance to which workers may be repeatedly exposed, for a normal 8-hour workday or a 40-hour week, day after day, without adverse effects. Any reference to TLV on safety data sheets is usually the TLV-TWA.

TLV-STEL (Short Term Exposure Limit). This is the maximum concentration of a substance to which workers may be exposed for a maximum period of 15 minutes. Four such exposures are allowed during a working day with an interval of at least one hour between each.

TLV-C (Ceiling). This is the upper limit above which workers should never be exposed to the substance.

The main ways that exposure can occur are as follows:

- Ingestion
  Generally the risk of swallowing significant quantities of liquid petroleum during normal operational practice is slight. If petroleum is swallowed, it causes acute discomfort and nausea. There is a possibility that liquid petroleum can be drawn into the lungs during vomiting and this can have serious consequences

- skin contact
  Petroleum products can cause skin irritation and may lead to dermatitis. They are also very irritating to the eyes and prolonged exposure can have serious effects. Direct contact with petroleum products must be avoided and proper PPE must be worn

- inhalation
  The main effect of petroleum gas inhalation on personnel is to produce narcosis. The symptoms range from eye irritation to headache and a feeling of light-headedness at higher concentrations. At very high concentrations, inhalation can lead to paralysis, insensibility or even death.

The toxicity of petroleum products depends on individual constituents. Toxicity can be greatly influenced by the presence of constituents like benzene and hydrogen sulphide. The smell of petroleum gases cannot be depended upon as an indicator of increasing concentrations, as in some cases the sense of smell may be dulled, especially if the mixture contains hydrogen sulphide. The absence of smell should never be taken to indicate the absence of vapour.

Ref: ISGOTT

KEY POINTS

♦ **Different types of pipeline systems exist for cargo operations on crude and product tankers**

♦ **the advantages and disadvantages of each type must be known to carry out safe loading and discharging operations.**

There are four basic types of pipeline systems in existence:

- Ring main
- direct line
- free flow
- cruciform.

Pipeline systems on individual tankers may consist of a mixture of one or more of the above types and will differ from other ships in terms of the positioning of the pumps and valves.

Ring Main

This is only found on older types of product tankers.

Advantages

- Versatile – any pump can be configured to discharge any tank
- good segregation – a high degree of tank separation is possible.

Disadvantages

- Expensive – both in construction and maintenance due to the large number of bends and joints required
- poor flow rate – due to the restriction imposed by the bends.

Direct Line

This pipeline system is generally found VLCCs.

Advantages

- Fast loading and discharge rates due to fewer bends
- cheap to construct
- low maintenance costs
- line washing time reduced.

Disadvantages

- Not very versatile and cannot handle two or more grades
- small number of valves can lead to poor segregation and less possibility of containing leaks.

Free Flow System

This system, which allows for very fast discharge and turnaround times, was generally fitted to large crude oil tankers such as VLCCs and ULCCs in the early 1970s, although it is rarely seen now because of its disadvantage of grade separation

Advantages

- Fast loading and discharging. There are sluice valves fitted in tank adjoining bulkheads, and these allow for very fast flow towards the pumproom when the ship is trimmed by the stern
- efficient line and tank drainage.

Disadvantages

- Carriage of more than one grade virtually impossible.

Master valve   Crossover valve   Tank valve

Ring Main

X Master valve   ⊠ Crossover valve   ▽ Tank valve

Direct Line

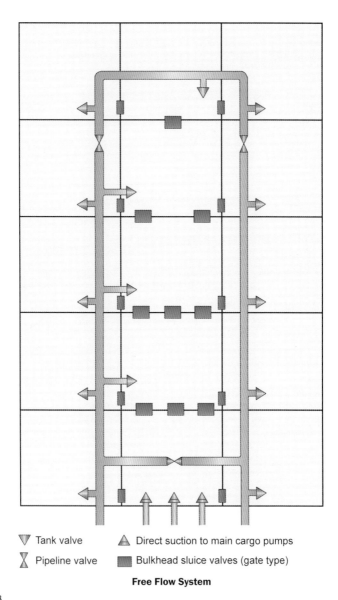

Tank valve   Direct suction to main cargo pumps

Pipeline valve   Bulkhead sluice valves (gate type)

Free Flow System

Cruciform System

This type of system combines the advantages of the ring main and the direct line systems and is now found on the majority of modern product carriers.

Advantages

- Very versatile, allowing two or more grades to be simultaneously loaded and discharged

- good segregation between grades
- possibility of interchanging system using spool pieces.

Disadvantages

- Expensive to install
- the large number of bends makes line cleaning difficult.

⊠ Master valve   ⊠ Crossover valve   ▽ Tank valve

Cruciform

KEY POINTS

♦ **Inert gas systems are a key component of the cargo handling process on tankers**

♦ **SOLAS Chapter II-2 regulates the technical and operational requirements for IG systems.**

Inert gas is a gas or a mixture of gases, such as flue gas, that contains insufficient oxygen to support the combustion of hydrocarbons. The main purpose of inert gas, in terms of cargo operations on tankers, is to prevent the formation of a flammable atmosphere in the cargo tanks. As can be seen in Chapter 2.1, the three components required for ignition are fuel, heat and oxygen. In atmospheres where the oxygen content is below 11.5% by volume, ignition is not possible. On a tanker, the cargo vapour is always present, which provides the fuel side of the fire triangle. Even though sources of ignition can be restricted, they can never be eliminated. Therefore, the best way to prevent combustion is to use inert gas and restrict oxygen. With an inert gas system, the protection against a tank explosion is achieved by introducing inert gas into the tank to keep the oxygen content low and so reduce to safe proportions the hydrocarbon gas concentration of the tank atmosphere.

As seen from the diagram below, when an inert gas is added to a hydrocarbon gas/air mixture (point F), the result

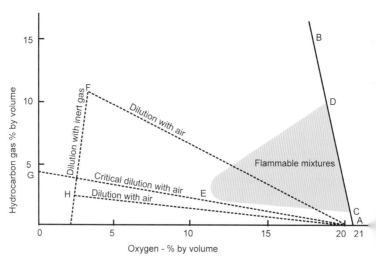

is a reduction in the concentration of hydrocarbons in the mixture to below the lower flammable limit (LFL), point H. At this point, air can safely be introduced into the tank as the concentration of hydrocarbons in the atmosphere will always be below the LFL until, finally, there is 21% oxygen in the tank, point A. The other alternative, diluting with air from point F, will cause the mixture to be within the flammable range, along line FA. Line AG is the Critical Dilution Line that divides the safe area below the LFL from the unsafe area immediately above.

Sources

The possible sources of inert gas on board a tanker are:

- The uptake from the main or auxiliary boilers
- an independent IG generator
- a gas turbine plant, when equipped with an after burner.

All the above sources should be able to deliver inert gas (IG), with a maximum oxygen content of less than 5% by volume, to the tanks.

Gas replacement processes

Replacement of gas in cargo tanks is needed for the following reasons:

- Inerting, to replace the air with inert gas
- purging, to replace inert gas with cargo vapours
- gas freeing, to replace inert gas with air.

These operations can be carried out using one of two processes of gas replacement, which are:

- Dilution
- displacement.

Dilution is a mixing process whereby the incoming gas mixes with the original gases to form a homogenous mixture throughout the tank. As a result, the concentration of the original gas decreases exponentially. The actual rate of gas replacement depends upon the volume flow of the incoming gas, its entry velocity and the dimensions of the tank.

Dilution Method of Replacing Tank Atmosphere

Displacement relies on a stable horizontal interface between the incoming gas and the replaced gas. Usually, the heavier inert gas is introduced from the bottom while the lighter air is vented from the top. As inert gas is introduced via the loading line, ie from the bottom of the tank, air is vented from the top of the tank. It is critical when using the displacement method to continually monitor the tank atmosphere and adjust flow rates to prevent mixing of the gases.

In practice, the best way to change atmospheres depends on the individual ship's cargo operating manual, recommendations, pipeline systems, IG equipment and practical experience.

Inert Gas System requirements
As per SOLAS Chapter II-2, Regulation 60, an inert gas system is required for the following ship types:

- All tankers of 20,000 DWT and upwards
- all tankers engaged in crude oil washing (COW).

The inert gas and associated venting system must allow for the following operations to be conducted safely (*Regulation 62 of SOLAS Chapter II-2*):

- Gas freeing
- purging
- inerting
- expansion and contraction of oil in the cargo tank
- cargo and ballast handling
- tank entry

- must be capable of supplying IG to all cargo tanks at a rate greater than the maximum discharge rate of the cargo (125%)
- must be capable of supplying IG with oxygen content less than 5% by volume in the inert gas supply main to the cargo tanks at any given rate of flow.

The following are the systems approved by SOLAS for IG systems:

- Treated flue gas systems from main or auxiliary boilers
- inert gas generators
- CO_2, but only where approved by the administration.

For double hull tankers, the double hull spaces must be fitted with suitable connections for the supply of air and, on ships fitted with an IG system, suitable connections for the supply of IG.

Scrubbing Tower
Flue gas cannot be introduced directly into the cargo tanks as it is at a temperature of about 300°C and contains a variety of impurities, including soot and sulphur dioxide. The function of the scrubbing tower is to cool and clean the flue gas, using sea-water, to remove the solid particles and reduce the sulphur dioxide content.

After leaving the boiler uptake, the gas enters the base of the scrubber. After passing through the pre-cooling water spray, the hot gas enters the base of the scrubber via a water seal. The hot gas then flows upwards through a zone of high capacity sprays and various impingement baffle plate stages.

IG control valve

Will permit the passage of inert gas to deck distribution system if:

- the oxygen content is 5% or less
- the pressure in the distribution main on the cargo tank side of the deck seal is below the pressure that the high level alarm activates
- the pressure in the distribution main on the cargo tank side of the deck seal is below the set pressure that the control valve opens.

Otherwise, it shall be diverted to the funnel or re-circulated.

IG Fans or Blowers
Rated to 125% capacity of the Cargo Pumps

Demister

Isolation valve

Blower inlet valve   Blower discharge valve

Return line

Flue Gas from Boiler
Dirty and full of particles. Seawater combines with hot exhaust gases and becomes acidic so pipes and scrubber are specially coated.

Scrubber tower and demister
Exhaust gas is quenched, cooled and cleaned using seawater spray. Coarse filters remove solid particles, thus reducing:

- sulphur dioxide by 90%
- solid particles by 95%
- temperature from 450°C to 3°C above seawater

Inert Gas System Layout

IG deck main
Normally one line, but a second line may be incorporated to prevent contamination between differing tank atmospheres.

Deck water seal non-return valve and IG crossover
Prevents dangerous back flow of IG and cargo vapour to the engine room. Must have two independent safety non-return arrangements.

IG tank isolation valve and blank
Each tank must be capable of being isolated and blanked atmospheres

Deck isolating valve

Tank pressure relief valve

Direct loading pipelines system
Situated forward of the non-return valves and capable of being blanked. Permits the introduction of gas to the bottom of the cargo tank for changing the atmosphere.

The system will have one or more connections so an IG supply from an external source can be used if necessary. There may also be connections and valves fitted that allow the segregated ballast tanks and pumproom to be inerted in the event of an emergency.

P/V breaker
Non-mechanical liquid sealing pressure vacuum relief device. Normally filled with a fresh water and glycol mix to prevent freezing.

Tank P/V valve
Independent to prevent over or under pressurisation of cargo tanks.

Mast riser
Manually operated, enabling venting when over pressurised.

IG Distribution System Deck

The gas finally exits at the top of the scrubber cooled to within 3° of the seawater temperature and with over 90% of soluble particles and sulphur dioxide removed. The gas then passes through demisters to remove any water entrained in the gas stream. The water extracted is drained overboard via a drain valve.

The following alarms are fitted:

- High water level
- low water level.

Fans

These are usually two high capacity blowers. They can be electric or turbine driven centrifugal fans. The fans have carbon gland seals to ensure gas tightness. The combined capacity of the fans must be at least 125% of the maximum discharge rate to satisfy SOLAS requirements. There is a fresh air intake valve before the blowers. This can be used to aerate the tanks after inerting once the IG system has been shut down.

Fixed Oxygen Analysers

Fixed oxygen monitors are fitted on the discharge side of the blowers. They have to be calibrated before use and they sound an alarm if the oxygen content exceeds the SOLAS maximum of 5% by volume.

Outflow of cooled, clean inert gas

Mesh type demister

Seawater inlets

Impingement plate stages

Venturi slot plate stage

Sprays

Inflow of hot boiler flue gas inlet

Effluent overboard

Submerged gas entry seal

Overflow troughs

Deck Water Seal

The purpose of the deck water seal is to prevent the backflow of hydrocarbon gases from the cargo tanks to the engine room and boiler uptakes via the IG main. A mechanical non-return valve may permit a small amount of hydrocarbon gas to pass through. To prevent this, the deck water seal is used, which is a non-mechanical non-return valve.

The basic form of deck water seal is the wet type, in which the gas passes through a water reservoir and a demister before exiting to the deck main. As long as the gas pressure is more than the pressure in the tanks, there is no danger of a backflow. In case the inert gas pressure falls, creating a danger of a backflow, the water forms a plug and hydrostatic head, preventing the flow of hydrocarbon gases back to the boiler uptakes.

The disadvantage of a 'wet' seal is that water carry-over may be high, resulting in increased corrosion. Therefore, a dry type or a semi-dry type may be used.

Normal flow

Water plug preventing backflow

Dry Type Seal

In a dry type seal, a sensor releases water from a holding tank if a loss of pressure is detected. The advantage is that there is no water carry over, but there is a risk of failure of the automatic control valves rendering the system ineffective.

Gas flow toward cargo tanks

Drop tank

Automatic valve control

Back pressure cargo tanks

Semi-Dry Type Seal

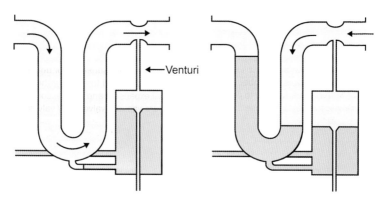

←—Venturi

In a semi-dry type deck water seal, the inert gas flow passing a Venturi draws the sealing water into a separate holding chamber by vacuum action, reducing the water carry-over. The disadvantage of this system is that a blockage of the Venturi tubes may allow water into the U-bend. Alternatively, a blockage of the tube leading to the U-bend may prevent water from entering the seal and render the system ineffective.

Mechanical Non-Return Valves

After the deck water seal, and as a further precaution to prevent the backflow of gases from the cargo tanks as well as to prevent any backflow of liquid that may enter the inert gas main if the cargo tanks are overfilled, a mechanical non-return valve is fitted. This should operate automatically at all times, and is generally in the form of a one-way flap. This valve may commonly be referred to as the 'Donkin' valve.

A separate deck isolating valve may be fitted forward of the non-return valve, so that the inert gas main can be isolated from the non-return valve for maintenance on the system.

Pressure/Vacuum Breaker

Air in - gas out

To and from tanks

Filling an level che connectic

A pressure vacuum breaker (P/V breaker) is fitted on the inert gas line to guard against over pressurisation or creation of a vacuum in the system.

The P/V breaker consists of an outer chamber mounted on a base on the main deck. The outer chamber is filled with a water/glycol mixture to prevent freezing in the winter. In case of over pressurisation, the liquid in the outer chamber is displaced relieving the IG line pressure. In case of under pressurisation, the liquid is drawn into the line, thus breaking the vacuum.

Pressure Vacuum Valves
In addition to the P/V breaker, to prevent over pressurisation or under pressurisation and to allow for the normal expansion and contraction of oil, pressure vacuum valves (P/V valves) are fitted on individual tanks or on individual mast risers connected to tanks.

Valve top

Valve housing

Stern

Pressure disc

Pressure seat

Vacuum housing

Vacuum disc

Flame screen

Vacuum seat

Flame arrester

The P/V valves are set to operate between 2100 mm water gauge (WG) pressure and 350 mm WG vacuum. If pressure increases, the pressure disc lifts venting IG and, in case of under pressurisation, the vacuum disc lifts allowing outside air to break the vacuum.

According to SOLAS Regulation 59, to prevent over pressurisation, a secondary P/V relief system is to be provided to back-up the primary P/V valves. Alternatively, tank pressure sensors can be installed with alarms for over or under pressure conditions.

While this valve is generally regarded as a back-up to the primary system, it is also an independent fail-safe system to protect the tank should it be isolated from the inert gas main.

Mast Risers
Mast risers are fitted to vent off inert gas or air to the atmosphere. Modern tankers are fitted with vapour recovery and vapour return systems. Mast risers are fitted with spark arresters as safety features. There is also an isolation valve at the base and, if the mast riser is for an individual tank, a pressure vacuum valve may be fitted.

Safety Features and Alarms for Inert Gas Systems
- Low water pressure/flow to the scrubber

- high water level in scrubber
- high IG temperature.

Any of these alarms should cause automatic shutdown of the blowers and regulating valves.

Other alarms required by SOLAS are:
- Failure of IG blowers (the gas regulating valve should close)
- O_2 content > 5% by volume
- failure of power supply to the regulating valve control system
- low water level in the deck water seal
- low IG pressure < 100 mm WG
- high IG pressure.

Additional requirements for IG generators:
- Insufficient fuel supply
- power failure to the generator
- power failure to the control system.

References:
Inert Gas Systems, 1990 edition, IMO London.
Petroleum Tankship Cargo Handling Manual; Lorne & Maclean; Polytech International, 1979.

2.4 Crude Oil Washing

Crude oil washing (COW) is the name given to the method of cleaning out the tanks on a crude oil tanker, by means of high-pressure jet nozzles, with the crude oil cargo itself ('oil to remove oil') at pressures of 9-10 kg/cm^2. This operation can take place either in port or at sea between discharge ports.

The solvent action of the crude oil makes the cleaning process far more effective than when only water is used. A subsequent water wash would be conducted prior to gas freeing the tank for entry or introduction of clean ballast. This system helps to prevent pollution of the seas from operational measures and maximises cargo outturn.

The requirement for new crude oil tankers to be built with double hulls has further improved the efficiency of COW operations because more of the structural support members are placed outside the cargo tanks, greatly reducing the amount of crude oil residues left in the tank following discharge.

MARPOL Requirements

MARPOL Annex I Regulation 13 (6) requires every new crude oil tanker of

Crude Oil Washing

20,000 tons DWT and above to be fitted crude oil washing systems.

On 'pre-MARPOL' tankers, ie those without segregated ballast tanks[1], the cargo tanks designated for dirty ballast[2] and clean ballast[3] must have been crude oil washed prior to the introduction of ballast water.

On ships with segregated ballast tanks, approximately 25% of the crude oil tanks need to be washed on every voyage for sludge control purposes, with no tank needing to be washed more than once in every four months.

Segregated Ballast Tanks (SBT) are ballast tanks with their own closed system that is segregated from the cargo oil system. These tanks are ballast tanks that only contain ballast water.
Dirty Ballast – This is the term for ballast water that has been loaded into a cargo tank that previously contained oil, but the tank has been crude oil washed.
Clean Ballast – This is the term for ballast water that has been loaded into a cargo tank that previously contained oil, but the tank has been crude oil washed and subsequently water washed.

For tankers with insufficient SBT capacity, an appropriate number of cargo tanks will need to be crude oil washed such that when subsequently water washed these tanks will be 'clean' enough (as defined by MARPOL) to take on sufficient water ballast to achieve the required draught on voyage.

The COW installation and arrangements onboard a tanker should comply with the provisions of the 'Specifications for the Design, Operation and Control of Crude Oil Washing Systems' adopted by the International Maritime Organization (IMO) in 1978.

In addition to these regulatory requirements, charter parties and commercial contracts may require the shipowner to carry out crude oil washing to a greater extent than legislation dictates in order to maximise the cargo outturn.

Operational Procedures

When it is necessary to carry out COW during cargo discharge, the Master must inform the terminal at least 24 hours in advance of the operation. COW should only be carried out when approval is received from the terminal.

Only fixed tank washing machines can be used to carry out COW. Prior to the operation, a safety checklist is completed. An inert gas system must be in operation and the oxygen content of the tank atmosphere must not exceed either 8% by volume or the minimum level required by the terminal. Personnel in charge of the operation must be qualified and must have completed an approved training course, either on board or in a training institution.

Crude Oil Wash Machine & Branch Line

Before arrival in port, the following must be carried out:

- Tank washing system pressure tested to normal working pressure and examined for leaks before arriving in port
- all machines should be operated and any leaks found should be made good.

During COW, the system must be kept under constant observation so that any leak can be detected and the necessary action taken.

Mixtures of oil and water can create an electrically charged mist during washing. Therefore, only 'dry'[4] crude should be used for COW and any tank that is to be used as a source for COW must be partly discharged (at least one metre) prior to operation. If the slop tank is to be used, it should first be completely discharged ashore and refilled with 'dry' crude oil.

Figure 1
Full wash.
Nozzle set to operate between 0° and 140°

Figure 2
Washing during discharge.
Tank one-third discharged.
Nozzle set to operate continuously between 60° and 140°

Figure 3
Tank two-thirds discharged.
Nozzle set to operate continuously between 25° and 75°

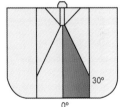

Figure 4
Bottom washing.
Nozzle set to operate continuously between 60° and 140°

[4] Dry Crude: Crude with minimum water content. In practice, before crude oil washing, tank soundings are reduced by about a metre (debottoming); this removes the free water which will settle below the crude oil in the tank. This is done to reduce the danger of static electricity when crude oil washing.

COW can cause excess hydrocarbon emissions. Subsequent ballasting of the tanks can cause this gas to be expelled to the atmosphere. Terminals may not allow this, so the following are among the means used to reduce vapour emission:

- Permanent ballast tanks of sufficient capacity
- retention of the gas in the cargo tank system by simultaneous ballasting and cargo discharge
- gas compression method
- on completion of the discharge, the tank pressure is at a minimum and all cargo tanks are common via the inert gas line
- gases from the ballasted cargo tanks are transferred through the inert gas lines into the available cargo tank space
- a suitable combination of any of these vapour methods.

Advantages of COW

- Increased cargo outturn as clingage and deposits are reduced
- reduction in the time for pre-dock cleaning
- reduces operational pollution
- minimum manual desludging required

- reduction in ballast passage tank cleaning
- less seawater discharged to shore
- less tank corrosion.

Disadvantages of crude oil washing

- Increased workload in port
- increase in discharge time
- increased vapour emissions
- additional training for crew required
- additional pipework, hence more possibilities of leaks
- higher capital costs for installation.

Possible COW abort situations

- Inert gas plant failure
- high oxygen content in tank
- failure of the oxygen detectors
- leakage in joint or pipeline
- tank overflow
- emergency alarms
- failure of the tank gauging system
- poor weather conditions
- failure of communications
- changes in ullage for tanks that are not being discharged
- hydrocarbon emissions in excess of terminal requirements.

KEY POINTS

♦ **Loading, discharging and cargo care on an oil or product tanker is a potentially hazardous operation**

♦ **procedures must be put in place and followed to ensure a safe operation.**

Before any cargo operations are carried out, the Master of the ship and the terminal operator must:

- Agree in writing the handling procedures, including the maximum loading and discharge rates

- complete and sign the ship/shore safety checklist, which shows the main safety precautions to be taken before and during the cargo transfer operation

- agree in writing the actions that are to be taken in the case of an emergency during the cargo transfer operation.

Completion of the ship/shore safety checklist ensures that the terminal and the ship have made the necessary preparations for the safe transfer of the cargo. Some of the checklist questions are directed at the terminal, some questions are for the ship and others apply to both ship and terminal. The checklist must not be signed until both parties are satisfied that the standards of safety on both sides are fully acceptable. Part 'A' of the checklist deals with bulk liquid general, which applies to all tankers. Parts 'B' and 'C' apply to chemical and gas tankers.

Loading
After completion of the ship/shore safety checklist, the cargo transfer

operations can commence. Prior to loading, the stability of the ship will be calculated and checked. As deballasting will be carried out concurrently with the loading operations, it must be ensured that there are no excessive free surface effects that could lead to a loss of stability. This is especially important for double hull tankers as the 'U' shaped ballast tanks can give rise to significant free surface effects when the water level falls below the wing tank level. Ballast and loading operations must be carried out in a way such that the ship's hull is never subject to excessive stresses.

Inert Gas Procedures
During loading, the inert gas plant must be closed down. Inert gas pressures in the tanks to be loaded must be reduced prior to the commencement of loading.

During loading, the following sequence of operations is carried out:

- Agree on maximum loading rates with the terminal

- ensure that the ship/shore safety checklist is completed

- ensure that an emergency shutdown procedure is agreed between the ship and the shore

- line-up according to the loading plan and double check the position of the valves

- for closed loading, ensure that the ullage, sounding and sighting ports are closed

- the IG displaced by the loading operation is usually vented to the atmosphere via the mast riser or, if the terminal is so equipped, the vapours can be returned ashore using a vapour return line

- when line-up is done and verified, the terminal must be informed and the manifold valves opened

- load initially at a slow rate, if possible by gravity

- check for leaks and that the correct tanks are being filled up

- when rate is increased, check for leaks again and ensure that the ship/shore connections are checked for tightness

- slowly increase the loading rate to maximum, continuously monitoring the manifold pressure

- deballasting operations are carried out concurrently.

Topping Off

Completion of loading to the required ullage is called 'topping off'. The following must be carried out when topping off:

- When loading, a 'stagger' is built into the tanks by throttling the individual tank loading valves. This ensures that all tanks do not finish at the same time and gives adequate time between tank finishing

- the ullage for the last tank to be topped off must take into account the amount of cargo in the line for draining purposes

- advise the shore when the final tanks are to be topped off and what the topping off sequence will be

- advise the shore in good time to reduce the loading rate sufficiently to permit effective control of the cargo flow

- after topping off individual tanks, the master valves must be shut to ensure segregation of cargo parcels

- always monitor ullages, including those of completed tanks, to ensure that spills and cargo overflow does not occur because of leaking valves

- the number of valves to be closed during the topping off period must be reduced to a minimum

- to prevent a pressure surge in the line, the tanker should not close all its valves against the flow of oil

- on completion of the final tank and line draining, the shore control valves must be closed before the ship's valves

- after loading has been completed, a responsible ship's officer must check that all valves in the cargo system are closed, all appropriate tank openings are closed and that the pressure vacuum relief valves are correctly set.

Loaded Voyage

During the loaded voyage, the cargo and associated spaces must be monitored continuously. The pressure/vacuum valves are usually set to automatic and, in the case of a low pressure alarm, the inert gas plant should be started to ensure a positive pressure of inert gas at all times. Some ships are equipped with a 'top-up' inert gas plant for this purpose.

In the case of a double hull tanker, the double hull spaces must be monitored for hydrocarbon content at least once per week. During the loaded passage, the ballast tanks should be sounded on a regular basis as a backup method of detecting any oil leakage.

Discharging

Before starting to discharge cargo, the ship and the terminal must formally agree that operations can be carried out safely. The appropriate section of the ship/shore safety checklist must be completed. The maximum discharge rates and manifold pressures must be agreed.

IG Operations

The inert gas system must be fully operational and producing good quality IG of less than 5% oxygen at the start of the discharge operation.

Cargo discharge must not be started until:

- All relevant cargo tanks, including slop tanks, are common with the inert gas main
- all other cargo openings, including the vent valves are securely closed
- the inert gas plant is operating
- the deck isolating valve is open and the fresh air intake is closed.

the event of the failure of the inert gas system, action must be taken to prevent any air being drawn into the tanks. All cargo and ballast operations must be stopped, the inert gas isolating valve must be closed and immediate action must be taken to repair the system.

COW

On crude oil tankers that intend to carry out COW during discharge operations, the lines are pressure tested to their working pressure of 9-10 kg/cm^2 and checked for leaks prior to arrival. The terminal is also informed about the need to wash and must allow this operation to be carried out unless there is reasonable cause not to do so. Other ancillary systems are also tested at this stage and the results logged.

Discharging Operations

During discharge, the following sequence of operations is usually carried out:

- The discharge plan is made and agreed by all parties
- complete the 'line-up' and double check that the correct valves are open
- the discharge plan must take into account any ballasting operations and, particularly on double hull tankers, the excessive free surface caused must be allowed for
- the inert gas system must be in operation, as detailed previously
- shore valves must be fully open before opening the ship's manifold valves
- start at a slow rate and confirm with the terminal that the flow of cargo is being received in the correct tanks

- check for any leaks and then, on the agreement of the terminal, increase the cargo loading rate
- If COW needs to be carried out, the plan must be incorporated into the discharge plan and a responsible officer must monitor the operation
- during discharge, the tanker, in agreement with the terminal, must control the flow of cargo. The discharge rate must not be substantially changed without the agreement of the terminal
- on completion of discharge, the ship's deck cargo lines must be drained into an appropriate tank and then discharged ashore or into a slop tank.

On completion of the discharging operation, and before the hoses or arms are disconnected, the ship's manifold valves and shore valves must be shut and the drain cocks at the vessel's manifolds should be opened to drain into fixed drain tanks or portable drip trays. The contents of portable drip trays must be transferred to a slop tank or other safe receptacle.

Reference: *ISGOTT*

KEY POINTS

♦ **Correct calculation of quantities is important to determine the cargo loaded and discharged**

♦ **the quantities have to be standardised to reference temperatures and densities.**

As oil expands when heated, an *ullage space* is kept above the liquid level to allow for such expansion. *Ullage* is the measurement between the surface of a liquid cargo and the top of the tank. Sometimes the measurement may be up to the top of the ullage port, in which case the tank sounding or ullage tables will allow for this. The quantities loaded can be calculated by referring to the ullage section in the tank calibration tables.

In the case of smaller ships, *soundings* may be taken instead of the ullage. A sounding is the measurement taken from the surface of the liquid to the bottom of the tank, ie the depth of liquid.

Both ullage measurements and soundings are affected by list and trim and tables that take account of this are used to correct the readings.

Measuring Ullage

The Relationship between Ullage and Sounding

The expansion effect shows that the density of oil is dependent on the temperature. At higher temperatures, the oil is less dense and occupies a greater space in the tanks.

The following is an example of a basic calculation to determine the weight of cargo to load and ullage at the time of loading, given the percentage expansion expected during the voyage:

> A tank of Length 28 m, Breadth 18.3 m and Depth 12 m is to be loaded with a vegetable oil of RD 0.830. The minimum ullage on passage is to be 0.27 m. Assuming a 3% expansion on passage, calculate:-
> 1) The ullage on loading
> 2) The weight of oil loaded.

Solution:

Final volume of oil:
28 m × 18.3 m × (12 m - 0.27 m)
= 6010.45 m^3

Volume of oil at loading =
6010.45/103% (expansion) =
5835.39 m^3

Depth of oil on loading (sounding)
= 5835.39/(28 × 18.3) = 11.39 m

Ullage on loading =
depth of tank − sounding =
112 − 11.39 = **0.61 m**

Weight of oil loaded =
Volume × Relative Density
= 5835. 39 m^3 × 0.830

= 4843.4 tonnes

What complicates matters onboard oil and product tankers is that the quantities calculated also include sediment and free water dissolved in the cargo. Also, the cargo is loaded and discharged at different temperatures and this will affect the density. To avoid confusion the density is calculated at certain reference temperatures. Unfortunately different countries have different reference temperatures. The following are the reference temperatures used in oil trading:

- In the US   60°F
- In Western Europe   15°C
- In Brazil and Eastern Europe 20°C

Ullage hatch

Ullage distance

GOV

TOV

FW

Hard-packed sediment

For volume measurement, two units exist. These are:

- The cubic metre (m^3) in metric countries
- The barrel (Bbl) in non-metric countries.

It is customary to refer to volumes at the reference temperatures, as follows:

- US barrels @ 60°F or cubic metres @ 15°C.

The following are the principal terms used in the measurement of oil cargoes:

Total Observed Volume (TOV)
This is the total volume of material measured in the tank including cargo (oil), free water (FW), entrained sediment and water (S&W) and sediment and scale as measured at ambient (observed) temperature and pressure.

Free Water (FW)
This is the water layer existing as a separate phase normally detected by

water paste or interface detector and usually settled at the bottom of the tank (depending on relative density of cargo).

Gross Observed Volume (GOV)
TOV less FW and bottom sediment, being the measured volume of oil and S&W at observed temperature and pressure. In practice, the bottom sediment is difficult to quantify and is ignored.

Gross Standard Volume (GSV)
Measured volume of oil and S&W at standard conditions of 15°C and atmospheric pressure. To obtain the GSV, in practice the GOV is multiplied by a volume correction factor. This is obtained from standard tables such as *ASTM*[1] *table 54*.

Net Standard Volume (NSV)
Normally applicable to crude oil, NSV is the GSV minus sediment and water (S&W). For products, S&W is not normally deducted and is included in the cargo figures.

Total Calculated Volume (TCV)

Total amount of oil, FW and S&W reported at standard temperature. In practice, TCV is the GSV plus the measured FW.

To calculate the amount of oil in a ship's cargo tanks using a predetermined temperature and the advised density, the volume correction factor (VCF) is determined from the American Society for Testing and Materials (ASTM) and Institute of Petroleum (IP) *Petroleum Measurement Tables.* The GOV is multiplied by the VCF to obtain the required GSV. Depending on the units in use, the VCF will standardise the oil volume to 15°C (m^3) or 60°F (US barrels).

ASTM/IP tables 6, 24 and 54 are generally used to establish the VCF for a given density and temperature. Each of the tables is produced in three versions:

- 'A' version - for generalised crude oils
- 'B' version - for generalised (petroleum) products
- 'C' version - for individual and special applications.

Once the ship's loaded figures have been determined, they must be compared with the shore figures. This comparison is known as the Vessel Load Ratio (VLR). Similarly, the Vessel Discharge Ratio (VDR) can also be determined at the discharge port. Using these figures, the Vessel Experience Factor (VEF) can be determined. The VEF is the historical difference in ship and shore figures over a given period, usually 10 loadings. Using the VEF, the chief officer can determine if the B/L quantity given is reliable. The VEF can change over a ship's lifetime due to the following:

- Change of trade
- accumulation of sediments
- descaling for dry docking
- any structural alterations to the ship or the tanks.

Each ship has a different VEF and it usually varies between –1% to +1% of the shore figures. The VEF of a vessel must be accurately determined and usually the IP method is used. This involves taking the mean of the past Vessel Load Ratio (VLR) readings and deleting the values that do not fall within 0.3% of this mean. Another mean is then taken and this is the declared VEF.

Reference: *Shipboard Petroleum Surveys, a Guide to Good Practice; Severn Anthony & the North of England P&I Association, Anchorage Press (UK) 1995.*

2.7 Chemical Cargoes

Chemical Tanker

Chemical cargoes carried in bulk can pose the following hazards:

- Toxicity
- reactivity
- corrosivity
- flammability
- pollution.

The *International Code for the Construction and Equipment of Ships Carrying Chemical Cargoes in Bulk* (IBC Code) regulates the carriage of these potentially dangerous substances

IBC Code

by sea and provides an international standard for the safe carriage in bulk of liquid chemicals.

The IBC Code applies to ships, regardless of size, engaged in the carriage of bulk cargoes of dangerous or noxious liquid chemical substances that have significant fire and other hazards in excess of those of petroleum cargoes.

The IBC Code applies to ships built on or after the 1st July 1986. For ships built before 1986, another version of the code, called the *BCH Code,* applies. The substances to which the requirements of the Code apply are listed in Chapter 17 of the Code. Chapter 16 deals with the operational requirements of chemical tankers and includes safety features that are peculiar to them.

The IBC Code is divided as follows:

- Survival capability and tank location
- ship arrangements
- cargo containment
- cargo transfer
- construction materials
- cargo temperature control
- tank venting and gas-freeing arrangements
- environmental control
- electrical installations
- fire protection and extinction
- mechanical ventilation
- instrumentation
- personnel protection
- special requirements
- operational requirements

- minimum requirements
- transport of wastes.

The basic philosophy of the Code is to class each chemical tanker by type, according to the degree of hazard presented by the products carried. The vessels are designed to minimise risk in the event of an incident of any kind, and will have sophisticated cargo monitoring systems and a high level of safety equipment.

Ship Types

The Code considers the possibility that damage to the vessel from collision or grounding may result in an uncontrollable release of cargo to the atmosphere with resultant pollution, fire or toxic risks. To minimise this risk, vessels are classified into three types:

- Type 1 (offering the highest level of protection) for the most hazardous cargoes
- Type 2 intermediate protection
- Type 3 the lowest form of protection for the least harmful chemicals.

Type 1 Ship

Designed for the carriage of Chapter 17 products with severe environmental and safety hazards that require maximum preventative measures to preclude an escape of the cargo. The design principle for these ships is that the cargo carrying compartments are located a minimum distance from the hull of the ship to guard against releas due to collision or grounding. The tank should be located at a distance not les than the breadth of the ship divided by 5, or 11.5 metres, whichever is less.

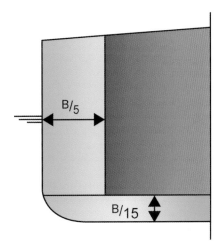

Type 2 Ship
Designed for the carriage of Chapter 17 products with appreciably severe environmental and safety hazards, which require significant preventative measures to preclude an escape of such cargo. The minimum distance of the cargo tanks is 760 mm from the side shell plating and B/15 or 6 metres from the moulded bottom plating.

Type 3 Ship

Designed to transport Chapter 17 products with sufficiently severe environmental and safety hazards that they require a moderate degree of containment to increase survival capability in a damaged condition. There are no restrictions for the location of cargo tanks in a type 3 ship.

Certification

An *'International Pollution Prevention Certificate for the Carriage of Noxious Liquid Substances in Bulk (NLS Certificate)'* is required by ships engaged in the carriage of noxious liquid substances for bulk trading internationally. This includes offshore supply vessels carrying noxious liquid substances in cargo tanks as well as product carriers carrying noxious liquid cargoes.

Certificate of Fitness

All chemical tankers will be issued with a certificate of fitness that details the name and port of registry of the vessel, type of vessel, cargoes that can be carried, and the conditions of carriage of the cargoes. Chemical tankers issued with this will not require an NLS certificate as the certificate of fitness will be treated with the same force.

Cargoes

The majority of chemical cargoes carried by sea are transported in small quantities. Because of this, chemical tankers are likely to have more than 30 different tanks. As many of these cargoes are not compatible with each other, the piping, ventilation and pumps are separate. Each tank usually contains a deepwell pump that is lubricated by the cargo itself. Tank coatings are also important as some cargoes can react with them. Newer ships have mainly stainless steel tanks as this material does not react with any chemical. However, certain cargoes such as chlorides, fluorides, and acids may remove the anti-corrosive properties of the steel. Other coatings include epoxy and zinc silicate. No matter what the coating of a tank is, none can guarantee against damage and they must be inspected regularly with any damage rectified immediately. Some epoxy coatings soften under the action of chemicals allowing the coating to absorb/retain some of the cargo. If this occurs, the tank must be ventilated and washed before loading the next cargo. Due to the reactive nature of many cargoes, an inhibitor may be added to stabilise the cargo.

Prior to loading a chemical cargo, the ship's certificate of fitness must be consulted to determine if the ship is allowed to load that type. Then Chapter 17 of the Code must be consulted, which lists the minimum requirements for that type of cargo including ventilation, gauging, fire protection and other special requirements.

Finally, other publications including the ship's *Procedures and Arrangements Manual* (P&A manual) will provide ship specific requirements for that type of cargo. For tank cleaning requirements, various industry guides exist, including one published by the US Coast Guard that lists the different procedures to be followed to prepare tanks for the specified cargo. Before cargo transfer operations are commenced, the *Ship/Shore Safety Checklist* is completed, including part 'B', which deals specifically with chemical cargoes.

Material Safety Data Sheets' (MSDS) provided by the shipper will detail the following information about the cargo:

- Appearance
- odour
- hazards
- emergency procedures
- fire and explosive data
- chemical data
- reactivity information
- health data
- physical properties
- handling and storage recommendations
- manufacturer's name
- emergency contact number.

Disposal of tank washings is governed by MARPOL Annex II. According to the present regulations, cargoes are divided into four categories, X, Y, Z and Other Substances (OS), depending on the severity of the pollution hazard. Category X cargoes have the most severe pollution hazards and are banned from being discharged into the sea. Category Z cargoes have the minimum hazards and justify fewer restrictions on discharge to the environment. Other substances are those not covered by X, Y or Z and are considered to have no threat to safety or the environment.

The 2007 revised Annex II specifies only the Antarctic as a Special Area. However, no discharge of residues containing noxious substances is permitted within 12 miles of the nearest land and more stringent restrictions apply to the Baltic and Black Sea areas.

All ships to which Annex II applies must carry and maintain a *Cargo Record Book*. This must be completed on a tank-to-tank basis for all cargo handling, tank washing and ballast operations. Any discharges into the sea, for whatever reason, must also be recorded. The Master and the officer in charge of the operation should sign each entry.

Inerting and Ventilation Requirements

All approved chemical tankers over 20,000 tonnes must have an IG plant. The venting system must be suitable for the cargo and must ensure that cargo vapour is neither able to accumulate on the decks nor enter the accommodation. For this reason, high velocity vents are used. Vapours must never be allowed to accumulate near sources of ignition.

Pipelines

Because of the complex nature of the cargoes carried, pipeline systems can be very intricate and there may be as many as 50 manifolds, depending on the number of cargoes that the ship can carry. There are crossover valves and spool pieces that can be used to interconnect between different pipeline systems. Segregation of cargoes is important, not only for safety reasons but also for commercial purposes. Double valve segregation is the minimum required and in many cases completely separate and independent systems may be required.

Instrumentation and Personal Protection

Modern chemical tankers have a centralised cargo control room allowing remote tank readings giving temperature, ullage, line pressure, valve positions, pump status and discharge rates. Valves, pumps and other cargo systems can be remotely operated from the cargo control room. For fire prevention purposes, a fixed foam based system is carried which is capable of covering the entire cargo deck area and will last for at least 30 min at the highest rate. For gas detection, at least two instruments capable of detecting toxic and flammable concentrations must be carried, one of which may be fixed. These must be calibrated for specific vapours.

For personal protection, the following equipment is required:

- Chemical-resistant suits
- face coverings, gas masks
- stored in special lockers.

Safety equipment sets (at least 3 sets carried):

- BA sets
- protective clothing
- fireproof, chemical-resistant lifeline
- explosion-proof lamp.

In addition, the following equipment is carried for use in case of spillages or other emergencies:

- Stretchers
- medical first aid equipment
- resuscitation equipment
- antidotes for cargoes carried
- decontamination showers and eyebaths on deck.

Reference: *IBC Code, ICS Tanker Safety Guide (Chemicals)*

Liquefied gases transported by sea are mainly of three types:

- Liquefied Petroleum Gases (LPG)
- Liquefied Chemical Gases
- Liquefied Natural Gas (LNG).

Liquefied Petroleum Gases

These are mainly propane and butane or a mixture of the two. They are normally used as fuel for heating or cooking. Both propane and butane are heavier than air and are highly flammable.

Liquefied Chemical Gases

These are gases such as vinyl chloride monomer, butadiene or ammonia, which are manufactured gases.

Liquefied Natural Gas

This is methane or ethane, used for heating and as fuel for power plants.

IGC Code

The 'International Code for the Construction and Equipment of Ships Carrying Liquefied Gases in Bulk' (IGC Code) provides an international standard for the safe carriage by sea of liquefied gases (and other substances listed in the Code) in bulk. The purpose of the code is to minimise risks to the ships, their crews and the environment. The Code also prescribes the design and constructional standards of such ships and the equipment they should

IGC Code

The Cargoes

The IGC Code defines liquefied gases as

> "Products having a vapour pressure exceeding 2.8 bar absolute at a temperature of 37.8 °C and other products shown in Chapter 19 of the Code and carried in bulk".

In practical terms, this means products that are gases at atmospheric pressure and ambient temperature. It is commercially and practically impossible to transport these substances in a gaseous state as, in the case of LNG, 1 m^3 of LNG liquid would occupy 600 m^3 as a gas. Therefore, the only practical way of transporting these substances in large amounts is in liquid form.

carry. The intent of this Code is in line with that of the *'International Code for the Construction and Equipment of Ships Carrying Dangerous Chemicals in Bulk' (IBC Code)*. A ship complying with the IGC Code can be issued with an International Certificate of Fitness, which signifies that a minimum standard of constructional equipment and some operational safety has been achieved.

There are three ways in which these substances can be transported in liquid form.

Fully Pressurised

This is where the gas is loaded in a pressure vessel and allowed to evaporate. When the pressure inside the cylinder reaches the critical pressure[1] for the gas, the gas liquefies and remains in that state as long as the pressure is maintained. Most LPG and chemical gases can be transported in this form. LNG cannot be commercially transported in large quantities in this form as the critical pressure for LNG is in excess of 45 bars.

The IGC Code applies to gas carriers constructed on or after 1 July 1986. Gas carriers constructed before that date are recommended to comply with the requirements of the *'Code for the Construction and Equipment of Ships Carrying Liquefied Gases in Bulk' (GC Code)* or the *'Code for Existing Ships Carrying Liquefied Gases in Bulk' (EGC Code)*. The basic philosophy of the Codes is to match a ship type with the hazards of the products transported.

Typical working pressures are between 15-17 atmospheres. The drawback with this type of containment is the

---

[1] *The pressure of a saturated vapour at the critical temperature (ie the pressure required to cause liquefaction at that temperature).*

A fully pressurised LPG carrier

heavy construction of the cylindrical or spherical pressure tanks and, due to the shape of the tanks, a great deal of hull space is wasted.

Semi-Refrigerated

LPG and chemical gases can be transported either in a pressurised or a refrigerated state. To make the maximum use of this property and to ensure flexibility of carriage, many LPG and chemgas ships are built with pressure tanks and reliquefaction plants. The ships are designed so that they can carry their LPG cargoes either fully refrigerated, fully pressurised or a partial combination of the two.

Fully Refrigerated

The other way to transport gases in their liquid form is to cool them down in shore tanks until the temperatures reach just below their boiling point. In this way, the liquefied gases can be transferred to the fully refrigerated ship, maintained at ship tank temperatures slightly above boiling point and transported at near to atmospheric pressure. As the gas will boil off during the voyage, a way of controlling this boil off is required. On LPG vessels, this is done by a reliquefaction plant,

75,000 m³ fully refrigerated LPG carrier with self-supporting prismatic tanks

Self-supporting prismatic tank
Fully refrigerated Type 'A' tank

Fully Refrigerated type 'A' Tank

which reliquefies the boil off and returns liquid back to the tank. Since very large pressures are required to reliquefy LNG and, as the table of properties shows LNG is lighter than air, on most LNG vessels the boil off is used as a fuel in the engine room. Recently there have been a few LNG vessels with onboard reliquefaction plants, but such ships are still rare.

The following table shows the physical properties of commonly carried gases in the refrigerated condition:

Properties	Ammonia	n-Butane	Propane	Butadiene
Carriage temperature °C (at boiling point)	-34	-1	-42.8	-5
Cargo pressure kg/cm² at boiling point	1.04	1.04	1.04	1.04
Specific gravity of liquid at STP	0.683	0.602	0.583	0.653
Vapour density relative to air at STP	0.587	2.09	1.55	1.88
Flammable limit % by Vol LFL-UFL	14~28	1.8~8.5	2.1~9.5	1.0~11.5
Flashpoint °C	-57	-60	-105	-60
Ignition temperature °C	635	365	470	415
Symbol	NH_3	C_4H_{10}	C_3H_8	C_4H_6

Ship Types

The *IGC Code* specifies the following ship types:

Type '1G' Ship

Designed to transport products indicated in Chapter 19 of the IGC Code, which require *maximum* preventive measures to preclude the escape of such a cargo, eg:

chlorine, ethylene oxide, methyl bromide, sulphur dioxide.

Type '2G' Ship

Designed to transport products indicated in Chapter 19 of the IGC Code which require *significant* preventive measures to preclude the escape of such a cargo, eg:

ethane, methane (LNG), ethylene.

Type '2PG' Ship

Designed to transport products indicated in Chapter 19 of the IGC Code on a vessel of 150 m or less in length, which require *significant* preventive measures to preclude the escape of such cargo, and where the products are carried in independent type C tanks designed for a *MARVS*[2] of at least 7 bar and a cargo containment system design temperature of - 55 degrees or above, eg:

ammonia, butadiene, butane, propane, etc.

Type '3G' ship

Designed to transport products indicated in Chapter 19 of the IGC Code, which require *moderate* preventive measures to preclude the escape of such cargo, eg:

nitrogen, refrigerant gases (CFC).

Tank Location

Severe collisions or groundings could lead to cargo tank damage and uncontrolled release of the product. Such release could result in evaporation and dispersion of the product and, in some cases, cause brittle fracture of the ship's hull. Therefore, the tanks on board type 1 and type 2 gas tankers are located at stipulated minimum distances away from the ship's hull and, for cargoes carried in the refrigerated form, a secondary barrier is required in most cases. For LNG, since cargoes are transported at very low temperatures (-160°C), it is important that any leakage does not come into contact with untreated surfaces as a brittle fracture and a subsequent hull failure will result.

Cargo Operations

Cargo operations on LPG and LNG tankers depend on the type of ship involved. Most LPG ships are provided with deepwell pumps, and the very large LPG and LNG ships are provided with submerged pumps. Fully and semi-refrigerated LPG ships are equipped with cargo compressors and reliquefaction plants to handle boil off. LNG vessels generally use the boil off gas as fuel to generate steam for the steam turbine plants or to power ancillary equipment such as steam powered mooring winches.

For a fully pressurised vessel carrying cargo at ambient temperatures, the

Maximum Allowable Relief Valve Setting

loading and discharging process is more straightforward as the tanks are designed to take pressures of up to 15-17 atmospheres. The cargo can be discharged by pressurising the tanks and, during loading, the cargo is allowed to evaporate in the tank until the gas liquefies due to the increased pressure.

In the case of a semi-refrigerated vessel, if the cargo is carried in a refrigerated form, the cargo compressors are used to reliquefy the boil off and return cold liquid back to the tank. Since the tanks are designed to handle pressure of up to 9 bars (many having less than this at 4.5 or 7 bar capability), the cargo can be

carried at intermediate temperatures and then cooled during the voyage if required.

The tanks of fully refrigerated ships, including LNG vessels, are not designed to handle pressure more than 0.3 bar above the atmospheric pressure. Pressures are monitored very closely during the initial stages of loading and, in the case of refrigerated vessels, the cargo compressors and the refrigeration system run at full capacity.

The following flowchart illustrates a typical cycle of operation for a gas tanker equipped with a reliquefaction plant from a dry-dock or repair yard back to a dry-dock or repair yard:

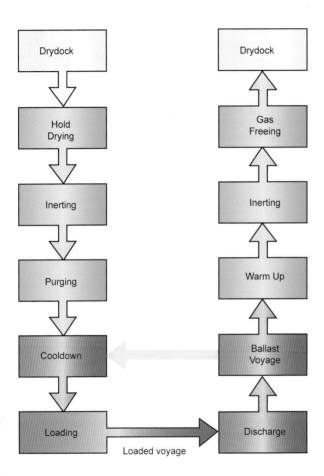

Hold Drying

On exiting a dry-dock or repair yard, the tanks are full of air at ambient temperature. Since the tanks will have to be cooled to accept the cargoes, it is necessary to reduce the dewpoint of the cargo to avoid the formation of ice and hydrates[3]. This is usually achieved by using an air drier.

Inerting

When the tank is full of dry air, the inerting process can be started. LPG ships are equipped with an inert gas

Hydrates are slush-like substances formed through a reaction with cold LPG. They can block pumps and jam valves.

generator that can generate IG with an oxygen content of less than 2%.

Purging

Purging is the replacement of the IG with vapours of the cargo to be loaded. Usually the denser cargo gas is introduced from the loading line and the IG is returned to the shore via the vapour line (although this procedure has, in the past, often been carried out without a vapour return to shore and with the ship venting at sea).

Cooldown

Tanks are cooled down to reduce the temperature of the cargo tank prior to loading in order to minimise thermal stresses and over pressurisation from excessive vaporisation. On refrigerated ships, the reliquefaction plant is used to draw vapours and return the cooled liquid via the spray line (see the following line diagram). On LNG vessels and ships that are on a dedicated route, with cargoes such as LPG or ammonia, some amount of cargo called *heel* is retained onboard from the last voyage and the tanks are kept cool for the next voyage. For initial cooling, cold liquid is introduced via the spray lines at a very slow rate while the thermal gradient inside the tank is monitored. Temperature gradients of 12-15°C may be experienced between the top and bottom plating of an LPG tank at this time, eg with -25°C at the top and -37°C at the bottom prior to loading a -42°C propane. The inherent risk of vapour flashing over pressurisation when the initial cold propane liquid enters the bottom of the tank is likely to require immediate shutdown and continued cooling/reliquefaction to bring the tank

under pressure control. The line drawing shows a typical arrangement.

Loading

After cooldown, the loading can commence, initially at a slow rate. The displaced vapours are either returned to shore or are reliquefied and sent back to the tank.

Loaded passage

During the loaded passage, the cargo pressures and temperatures are monitored and the cargo boil off reliquefied for quantity control. In semi-pressured ships with refrigeration capability, the cargo liquid may even be cooled down for arrival, depending on the charter party requirements.

Ballast voyage

During the ballast voyage on an LNG vessel, the tanks are kept cool by extracting the boil off gas generated by the heel left on board. In the case of most other gas ships, the ballast voyage may also involve preparation for a change of cargo.

Preparation for drydock

This involves warming up the tanks by using vapour heaters and puddle heating coils, then displacing the gas with IG in preparation for aerating and making tanks ready for inspection.

Safety and Personal Protection

Because of the hazardous nature of the cargoes carried, gas carriers are built to the highest safety standards and have alarms and instrumentation designed to be fail-safe. The basic principle of safe transportation of

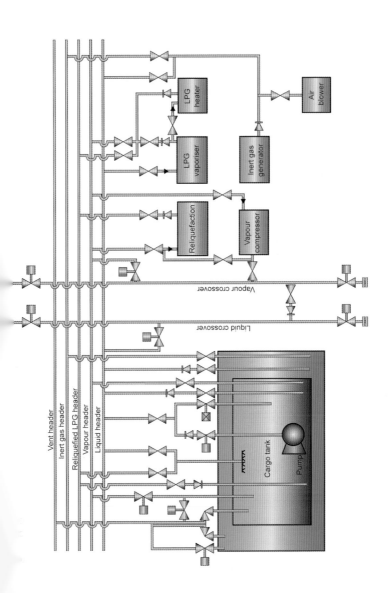

liquefied gas is not to allow a flammable atmosphere to form in the tanks at any time. This is achieved by carrying out all cargo operations in a closed cycle and keeping a positive pressure in the tanks to prevent the entry of air and oxygen. At all times during cargo operations, the space above the liquefied gas is filled with the vapour of the cargo. Since the atmosphere is over rich and there is no oxygen present, combustion cannot occur.

The ships are equipped with various safety and monitoring systems to avoid any untoward incidents. Emergency Shutdown systems (ESD) are linked to high level alarms, tank pressure alarms and heat sensors and, on activation, shut down the pumps and associated systems and close the manifold valves. On LNG ships, the ship ESD system is linked to the shore ESD system to coordinate shutdown and avoid pressure surges. Variations of this can be found at some ship/shore interface locations dealing with other gas ship types and it has been recommended that all such locations should adopt this practice.

The ship is divided into gas dangerous and gas safe areas, as shown in the following diagram, and fixed gas monitoring equipment is installed in the gas dangerous areas to detect any leaks. The interbarrier spaces (spaces between the tanks and the hull) are filled with IG, and fixed gas detectors and pressure detectors also monitor these spaces.

For personal protection, water spray systems are provided along with fixed and portable gas detectors and chemical suits, eye baths and decontamination showers. For cargo related fire-fighting on gas ships, dry powder is used. Fixed monitors are provided and a supply of dry powder is available to fight fires on deck. Additional medical equipment is also provided for treatment of any exposure to the cargo.

Reference: *Liquefied Gas Handling Principles on Ships and in Terminals - 3rd edition and SIGTTO website (www.sigtto.org).*

■ Gas dangerous zones

□ Gas dangerous spaces

▓ Gas safe spaces and zones

1. Cargo tank
2. Ventilation outlet from compressor room
3. Vent mast outlet
4. Cargo pipelines

Annexes

Principles and Operational Guidance for Deck Officers in Charge of a Watch in Port

Recommendations and Principles and Operational Guidance for Deck Officers in Charge of a Watch in Port

This recommendation applies to ships that are safely moored or safely anchored under normal circumstances in port and where the master has decided in the prevailing conditions that a navigational watch need not be kept.

Watch arrangements

1. Arrangements for keeping a watch when the ship is in port should:

    a. Ensure the safety of life, ship, cargo and port.

    b. Observe international, national and local rules.

    c. Maintain order and the normal routine of the ship.

2. The ship's Master should decide the composition and duration of the watch, depending on the conditions of mooring, type of ship and character of duties.

3. A qualified deck officer should be in charge of the watch, except in ships under 500 GRT not carrying dangerous cargo, in which case the Master may appoint whoever has appropriate qualifications to keep the watch in port.

4. The necessary equipment should be so arranged as to provide for efficient watch keeping.

Taking Over the Watch

5. The officer of the watch should not hand over the watch to the relieving officer if he has any reason to believe that the latter is obviously not capable of carrying out his duties effectively, in which case he should notify the Master accordingly.

6. The relieving officer should be informed of the following by the officer being relieved:

    a. The depth of water at the berth ship draft, the level and time of high and low waters, fastening of the moorings, arrangement of anchors and the slip of the chain and other features of mooring important for the safety of the ship; status main engines and availability for emergency use.

    b. All work to be performed on board the ship, the nature, amount and disposition of cargo loaded or remaining or any residue on board after unloading the ship.

    c. The level of water in bilges and ballast tanks.

    d. The signals or lights being exhibited.

    e. The number of crew members required to be onboard and the presence of any other person on board.

    f. The state of fire fighting appliances.

    g. Any special port regulations.

    h. The Master's standing and special orders.

    i. The lines of communication that are available between the ship and the dock staff of port authorities in the event of an emergency arising or assistance being required.

j. Other circumstances of importance to the safety of the ship and protection of the environment from pollution.

7. The relieving officer should satisfy himself that:

a. Fastenings of moorings or anchor chain are adequate

b. The appropriate signals or lights are properly hoisted and exhibited.

c. Safety measures and fire protection regulations are being maintained.

d. He is aware of the nature of any hazardous or dangerous cargo being loaded or discharged and the appropriate action in the event of any spillage or fire

e. No external conditions or circumstances imperil the ship and that his own ship does not imperil others.

8. If at the moment of handing over the watch, an important operation is being performed it should be concluded by the officer being relieved, except when ordered otherwise by the Master.

Keeping a Watch

9. The officer of the watch should

a. Make rounds to inspect the ship at appropriate intervals.

b. Pay particular attention to:

i. The conditions and fastening of the gangway, anchor chain or moorings, especially at the turn of the tide or in berth with a large rise and fall and if necessary take measures to ensure that they are in normal working condition.

ii. The draught, under keel clearance and the state of the ship to avoid dangerous listing or trim during cargo handling or ballasting.

iii. The state of the weather and sea.

iv. Observance of all regulations concerning safety precautions and fire protection.

v. Water level in bilges and tanks.

vi. All persons on board and their location, especially those in remote or enclosed spaces.

vii. The exhibition of any signals or lights.

c. In bad weather or on receiving a storm warning, take the necessary measures to protect the ship, personnel and cargo.

d. Take every precaution to prevent pollution of the environment by his own ship.

e. In an emergency threatening the safety of the ship, raise the alarm, inform the Master, take all possible measures to prevent any damage to the ship and, if necessary, request assistance from the shore authorities or neighbouring ships.

f. Be aware of the state of stability so that in the event of fire, the shore fire fighting authority may be advised of the approximate quantity of water that can be pumped on board without endangering the ship

g.   Offer assistance to ships or persons in distress.

h.   Take necessary precautions to prevent accidents or damage when the propellers are to be turned.

i.   Enter in the appropriate log book all important events affecting the ship.

'nciples for the keeping of a safe watch in port' is based on the withdrawn M Notice 1016. However, the dance contained within it remains a valuable and valid reference source.

153

MARINE GUIDANCE NOTE

MGN 60 (M)

Code of Safe Practice for Solid Bulk Cargoes (BC Code): 1996 Amendment

Carriage of Coal Cargoes

Notice to operators, shipowners, charterers, managers, masters, ship's officers and shippers.

Summary:

This Marine Guidance Note draws attention to the important changes to the provisions on the carriage of coal cargoes in the 1996 amendment of the BC Code.

1. The 1996 amendment of the IMO: Code of Safe Practice for Solid Bulk Cargoes (BC Code) includes changes to the individual schedule for Coal in Appendix B and a new Appendix G on Procedures for gas monitoring of Coal Cargoes.

2. Coal cargoes may emit methane gas which is flammable. A methane/air mixture containing between 5% and 16% methane constitutes an explosive atmosphere that can be ignited by sparks or naked flame. Accumulation of this gas in the hold may also result in leakage into adjacent spaces. Normally all holds should be surface ventilated for the first 24 hours after departure from the loading port. If the methane concentration is found to be acceptably low at the end of this period the ventilators are closed. On the other hand, if the concentration of methane as measured is over 20% of the LEL (Lower Explosive Limit), adequate surface ventilation is to be maintained to reduce the concentration.

3. Some coals may be subject to self-heating. To control the start of potential self-heating the hatches are kept closed and surface ventilation is limited to the absolute minimum time to remove any accumulated methane. Any self-heating is indicated by increasing concentration of carbon monoxide in the hold.

4. The Code requires that prior to departure the cargo should be trimmed reasonably level to the boundaries of the cargo space to avoid the formation of gas pockets and to prevent air permeating the body of the coal. This aspect is sometimes ignored in the rush to sail from the port and untrimmed holds can contribute to self-heating during the voyage.

5. Ships engaged in the carriage of coal should carry on board an instrument for measuring methane, oxygen and carbon monoxide gas concentrations so that the atmosphere within the cargo space may be monitored. The ships should also be provided with equipment suitable for taking a sample to be read by the

instrument and sampling points sited on the hatch coamings as high as possible in accordance with Appendix G of the BC Code.

6.   The individual schedule for coal provides detailed guidance on handling of coal cargoes and the Appendix G on the procedures for monitoring the gases. These are annexed to this note for ready reference.

7.   Safety, when carrying coal cargoes, cannot be taken for granted. The equipment should be serviced and instruments calibrated at regular intervals in accordance with the manufacturer's instructions and the ship staff trained in the use of the equipment. Regular gas monitoring of the cargoes provides the necessary information for detecting at an early stage potential problems and following appropriate procedures for safe carriage.

8.   With the exception of ships engaged on coastal voyages of short duration which need not be provided with carbon monoxide gas monitoring equipment, all ships engaged in the trade should be provided with the equipment and fitted out as required by the Code as soon as possible. Shipowners, masters and shippers are requested to note the changes and to observe the new provisions of the Code in cargo operations.

9.   The Code of Safe Practice for Solid Bulk Cargoes (BC Code) is a publication of the International Maritime Organization and can be obtained from the International Maritime Organization, 4 Albert Embankment, London SEI 7SR.

MSASD
Marine Safety Agency
Spring Place
105 Commercial Road
Southampton SO15 1EG

Tel 02380 329176
Fax 02380 329204
February 1998
MS54/02/08
©Crown Copyright 1998

An excutive agency of the Department of the Enviroment, Transport and the Regions

COAL[1]

(See also appendix A)

BC No.	IMO class	MFAG table no.	Approximate stowage factor (m7t)	EmS no.
010	MHB	311,616[2]	0.79 to 1.53	B14

Properties and characteristics

1.   Coals may emit methane, a flammable gas. A methane/air mixture containing between 5% and 16% methane constitutes an explosive atmosphere which can be ignited by sparks or naked flame, e.g. electrical or frictional sparks, a match or lighted cigarette. Methane is lighter than air and may, therefore, accumulate in the upper region of the cargo space or other enclosed spaces. If the cargo space boundaries are not tight, methane can seep through into spaces adjacent to the cargo space.

2.   Coals may be subject to oxidation, leading to depletion of oxygen and an increase in carbon dioxide in the cargo space (see also section 3 and appendix F).

3.   Some coals may be liable to self-heating that could lead to spontaneous combustion in the cargo space. Flammable and toxic gases, including carbon monoxide, may be produced. Carbon monoxide is an odourless gas, slightly lighter than air, and has flammable limits in air of 12% to 75% by volume. It is toxic by inhalation, with an affinity for blood haemoglobin over 200 times that of oxygen.

4.   Some coals may be liable to react with water and produce acids which may cause corrosion. Flammable and toxic gases, including hydrogen, may be produced. Hydrogen is an odourless gas, much lighter than air, and has flammable limits in air of 4% to 75% by volume.

Segregation and stowage requirements

1.   Boundaries of cargo spaces where materials are carried should be resistant to fire and liquids.

2.   Coals should be "separated from" goods of classes 1 (division 1.4), 2, 3, 4, and 5 in packaged form (see IMDG Code) and "separated from" solid bulk materials of classes 4 and 5.1.

3.   Stowage of goods of class 5.1 in packaged form or solid bulk materials of class 5.1 above or below a coal cargo should be prohibited.

4.   Coals should be "separated longitudinally by an intervening complete compartment or hold from" goods of class 1 other than division 1.4.

Note: For the interpretation of the segregation terms see paragraph 9.3.3.

[1] *For comprehensive information on transport of any material listed, refer to sections 1-10 of this Code.*
[2] *Refer to paragraph 6.1.1 (Asphyxia) of the MFAG*

General requirements for all coals

1. Prior to loading, the shipper or his appointed agent should provide in writing to the master the characteristics of the cargo and the recommended safe handling procedures for loading and transport of the cargo. As a minimum, the cargo's contract specifications for moisture content, sulphur content and size should be stated, and especially whether the cargo may be liable to emit methane or self-heat.

2. The master should be satisfied that he has received such information prior to accepting the cargo. If the shipper has advised that the cargo is liable to emit methane or self-heat, the master should additionally refer to the "Special precautions".

3. Before and during loading, and while the material remains on board, the master should observe the following:

    .1   All cargo spaces and bilge wells should be clean and dry. Any residue of waste material or previous cargo should be removed, including removable cargo battens, before loading.

    .2   All electrical cables and components situated in cargo spaces and adjacent spaces should be free from defects. Such cables and electrical components should be safe for use in an explosive atmosphere or positively isolated.

    .3   The ship should be suitably fitted and carry on board appropriate instruments for measuring the following without requiring entry in the cargo space:

        .3.1   concentration of methane in the atmosphere;

        .3.2   concentration of oxygen in the atmosphere;

        .3.3   concentration of carbon monoxide in the atmosphere; and

        .3.4   pH value of cargo hold bilge samples.

        These instruments should be regularly serviced and calibrated. Ship personnel should be trained in the use of such instruments. Details of gas measurement procedures are given in appendix G.

    .4   It is recommended that means be provided for measuring the temperature of the cargo in the range 0°C to 100°C. Such arrangements should enable the temperature of the coal to be measured while being loaded and during the voyage without requiring entry into the cargo space.

    .5   The ship should carry on board the self-contained breathing apparatus required by SOLAS regulation 11-2/17. The self-contained breathing apparatus should be worn only by personnel trained in its use (see also section 3 and appendix F).

    .6   Smoking and the use of naked flames should not be permitted in the cargo areas and adjacent spaces and appropriate warning notices should be posted in conspicuous places. Burning, cutting, chipping, welding or other sources of ignition should not be permitted in the vicinity of cargo spaces or in other adjacent spaces, unless the space has been properly ventilated and the methane gas measurements indicate it is safe to do so.

.7   The master should ensure that the coal cargo is not stowed adjacent to hot areas.

.8   Prior to departure, the master should be satisfied that the surface of the material has been trimmed reasonably level to the boundaries of the cargo space to avoid the formation of gas pockets and to prevent air from permeating the body of the coal. Casings leading into the cargo space should be adequately sealed. The shipper should ensure that the master receives the necessary co-operation from the loading terminal (see also section 5).

.9   The atmosphere in the space above the cargo in each cargo space should be regularly monitored for the presence of methane, oxygen and carbon monoxide. Details of gas monitoring procedures are given in appendix G. Records of these readings should be maintained. The frequency of the testing should depend upon the information provided by the shipper and the information obtained through the analysis of the atmosphere in the cargo space.

.10   Unless expressly directed otherwise, all holds should be surface ventilated for the first 24 hours after departure from the loading port. During this period, one measurement should be taken from one sample point per hold.

If after 24 hours the methane concentrations are at an acceptably low level, the ventilators should be closed. If not, they should remain open until acceptably low levels are obtained. In either event, measurements should be continued on a daily basis.

If significant concentrations of methane subsequently occur in unventilated holds, the appropriate special precautions as described in section 2.2.1 should apply.

.11   The master should ensure, as far as possible, that any gases which may be emitted from the materials do not accumulate in adjacent enclosed spaces.

.12   The master should ensure that enclosed working spaces, e.g. store-rooms, carpenter's shop, passage ways, tunnels, etc., are regularly monitored for the presence of methane, oxygen and carbon monoxide. Such spaces should be adequately ventilated.

.13   Regular hold bilge testing should be systematically carried out. If the pH monitoring indicates that a corrosion risk exists, the master should ensure that all bilges are kept dry during the voyage in order to avoid possible accumulation of acids on tank tops and in the bilge system.

.14   If the behaviour of the cargo during the voyage differs from that specified in the cargo declaration, the master should report such differences to the shipper. Such reports will enable the shipper to maintain records on the behaviour of the coal cargoes, so that the information provided to the master can be reviewed in the light of transport experience.

.15   The Administration may approve alternative requirements to those recommended in this schedule.

Special precautions

1. *Coals emitting methane*

If the shipper has advised that the cargo is liable to emit methane or analysis of the atmosphere in the cargo space indicates the presence of methane in excess of 20% of the lower explosion limit (LEL) the following additional precautions should be taken:

.1 Adequate surface ventilation should be maintained. On no account should air be directed into the body of the coal as air could promote self-heating.

.2 Care should be taken to vent any accumulated gases prior to removal of the hatch covers or other openings for any reason, including unloading. Cargo hatches and other openings should be opened carefully to avoid creating sparks. Smoking and the use of naked flame should be prohibited.

.3 Personnel should not be permitted to enter the cargo space or enclosed adjacent spaces unless the space has been ventilated and the atmosphere tested and found to be gas-free and to have sufficient oxygen to support life. If this is not possible, emergency entry into the space should be undertaken only by trained personnel wearing self-contained breathing apparatus, under the supervision of a responsible officer. In addition, special precautions to ensure that no source of ignition is carried into the space should be observed (see also section 3 and appendix F).

.4 The master should ensure that enclosed working spaces, e.g. store-rooms, carpenter's shops, passage ways, tunnels, etc., are regularly monitored for the presence of methane. Such spaces should be adequately ventilated and, in the case of mechanical ventilation, only equipment safe for use in an explosive atmosphere should be used. Testing is especially important prior to permitting personnel to enter such spaces or energizing equipment within those spaces.

2. *Self-heating coals*

.1 If the shipper has advised that the cargo is liable to self-heat, the master should seek confirmation that the precautions intended to be taken and the procedures intended for monitoring the cargo during the voyage are adequate.

.2 If the cargo is liable to self-heat or analysis of the atmosphere in the cargo space indicates an increasing concentration of carbon monoxide then the following additional precautions should be taken:

.2.1 The hatches should be closed immediately after completion of loading in each cargo space. The hatch covers can also be additionally sealed with a suitable sealing tape. Surface ventilation should be limited to the absolute minimum time necessary to remove methane which may have accumulated. Forced ventilation should not be used. On no account should air be directed into the body of the coal as air could promote self-heating.

.2.2   Personnel should not be allowed to enter the cargo space, unless they are wearing self-contained breathing apparatus and access is critical to the safety of the ship or safety of life. The self-contained breathing apparatus should be worn only by personnel trained in its use (see also section 3 and appendix F).

.2.3   When required by the competent authority, the carbon monoxide concentration in each cargo space should be measured at regular time intervals to detect self-heating.

.2.4   If at the time of loading, when the hatches are open, the temperature of the coal exceeds 55°C, expert advice should be obtained.

.2.5   If the carbon monoxide level is increasing steadily, a potential self-heating may be developing. The cargo space should be completely closed down and all ventilation ceased. The master should seek expert advice immediately. Water should not be used for cooling the material or fighting coal cargo fires at sea, but may be used for cooling the boundaries of the cargo space.

.2.6   Information to be passed to owners.

The most comprehensive record of measurements will always be the log used to record daily results. The coal cargo monitoring log for the voyage should be faxed, or the appropriate content should be telexed to the vessel's owners.

The following minimum information is essential if an accurate assessment of the situation is to be achieved.

(a)   identity of the holds involved; monitoring results covering carbon monoxide, methane and oxygen concentrations;

(b)   if available, temperature of coal, location and method used to obtain results;

(c)   time gas samples taken (monitoring routine);

(d)   time ventilators opened/closed;

(e)   quantity of coal in hold(s) involved;

(f)   type of coal as per shipper's declaration, and any special precautions indicated on declaration;

(g)   date loaded, and ETA at intended discharge port (which should be specified); and

(h)   comments or observations from the ship's master.

Procedures for Gas Monitoring of Coal Cargoes

G.1 Observations

Carbon monoxide monitoring, when conducted in accordance with the following recommendations, will provide a reliable early indication of self-heating within a coal cargo. This allows preventive action to be considered without delay. A steady rise in the level of carbon monoxide detected within a hold is conclusive indication that self-heating is taking place.

All vessels engaged in the carriage of coal should carry on board an instrument for measuring methane, oxygen and carbon monoxide gas concentrations (general requirements for all coals, section 3.3 in the coal entry, appendix B), so that the atmosphere within the cargo space may be monitored. This instrument should be regularly serviced and calibrated in accordance with the manufacturer's instructions. When properly maintained and operated, this instrument will provide reliable data about the atmosphere within the cargo space. Care needs to be exercised in interpreting methane measurements carried out in the low oxygen concentrations often found in unventilated cargo holds. The catalytic sensors normally used for the detection of methane rely on the presence of sufficient oxygen for accurate measurement. This phenomenon does not affect the measurement of carbon monoxide, or measurement of methane by infrared sensor. Further guidance may be obtained from the instrument manufacturer.

G.2 Sampling and measurement procedure

G.2.1 *Equipment*

An instrument is required which is capable of measuring methane, oxygen and carbon monoxide concentrations. The instrument should be fitted with an aspirator, flexible connection and a length of tubing to enable a representative sample to be obtained from within the square of the hatch. Stainless steel tubing approximately 0.5 m in length and 6 mm nominal internal diameter with an integral stainless steel threaded collar is preferred. The collar is necessary to provide an adequate seal at the sampling point.

A suitable filter should be used to protect the instrument against the ingress of moisture as recommended by the manufacturer. The presence of even a small amount of moisture will compromise the accuracy of the measurement.

G 2.2 *Siting of sampling points*

In order to obtain meaningful information about the behaviour of coal in a hold, gas measurements should be made via one sample point per hold. To ensure flexibility of measurement in adverse weather, however, two sample points should be provided per hold, one on the port side and one on the starboard side of the hatch cover (refer to figure G.2.7). Measurement from either of these locations is satisfactory.

Each sample point should comprise a hole of diameter approximately 12 mm

Figure G.2.7 Diagram of gas sampling point

positioned as near to the top of the hatch coaming as possible. It should be sealed with a screw cap to prevent ingress of water and air. It is essential that this cap is securely replaced after each measurement to maintain a tight seal.

The provision of any sample point should not compromise the seaworthiness of the vessel.

G 2.3 *Measurement*

Ensure that the instrument is calibrated and working properly in accordance with the manufacturer's instructions. Remove the sealing cap, insert the stainless steel tube into the sampling point and tighten the integral cap to ensure an adequate seal. Connect the instrument to the sampling tube. Draw a sample of the hold atmosphere through the tube, using the aspirator, until steady readings are obtained. Log the results on a form which records cargo hold, date and time for each measurement.

G.2.4 *Measurement strategy*

The identification of incipient self-heating from measurement of gas concentrations is more readily achieved under unventilated conditions. This is not always desirable because of the possibility of the accumulation of methane to dangerous concentrations. This is primarily, but not exclusively, a problem in the early stages of a voyage. Therefore it is recommended that holds are initially ventilated until measured methane concentrations are at an acceptably low level.

G.2.5 *Measurement in unventilated holds*

Under normal conditions one measurement per day is sufficient as a precautionary measure. However, if carbon monoxide levels are higher than 30 ppm then the frequency should be increased to at least twice a day at suitably spaced intervals. Any additional results should be logged.

If the carbon monoxide level in any hold reaches 50 ppm a self-heating condition may be developing and the owners of the vessel should be notified.

G.2.6 *Measurement in ventilated holds*

If the presence of methane is such that the ventilators are required to remain open, then a different procedure should be applied to enable the onset of any incipient self-heating to be detected.

To obtain meaningful data the ventilators should be closed for a period before the measurements are taken. This period may be chosen to suit the operational requirements of the vessel, but it is recommended that it is not less than four hours. It is vital in the interests of data interpretation that the shutdown time is constant whichever time period is selected. These measurements should be taken on a daily basis. If the carbon monoxide results exhibit a steady rise over three consecutive days, or exceed 50 ppm on any day, the owners of the vessel should be notified.

MARINE GUIDANCE NOTE

MGN 223 (M)

Maritime and Coastguard Agency

Carriage of coconut oil and other vegetable oils as cargo in tanks

Notice to Ship Owners, Operators and Managers, Masters and Officers of Merchant Ships and Offshore Installation Managers/Duty Holders and Shippers to the Offshore Industry

---

Summary

- Information has been received about unforeseen hazardous conditions that may arise when coconut oil and other vegetable oils are carried in the cargo or deep tanks of ships.

- This Marine Guidance Note draws attention to the hazards and makes recommendations to ensure safe working practices when handling such cargoes.

---

1. A report has been received about a serious accident that occurred on board a ship discharging a cargo of Indonesian crude coconut oil in a North European Port.

2. Six men hired from ashore entered one of the tanks nearing completion of discharge to sweep the residue towards the pump suction.

3. Within a few minutes, the workmen appeared to be in difficulties. Four were able to leave the tank but the other two collapsed over the heating coils. Both men suffered serious burns from the heating coils. One of them subsequently died.

4. The tank atmosphere was tested immediately after the accident for oxygen deficiency and flammability and found to be safe from those hazards.

5. However, very large concentrations of carbon monoxide (CO) were measured -more than 1000 - parts per million. As yet, there is no clear explanation for the presence of CO in the tank, though oxygen deficiency in tanks carrying such cargoes is well known.

6. A likely explanation is that the temperature of the heating coils had reached levels high enough to generate CO from the reducing quantity of cargo in the tank during the discharging process.

7. The Maritime and Coastguard Agency (MCA) therefore recommends that before such spaces are entered, the full range of precautions for entry into enclosed spaces described in the Code of Safe Working Practices for Merchant Seamen (section 17) or the International Maritime Organisation Assembly Resolution A.864(20) entitled Recommendations for Entering Enclosed Spaces Aboard Ship are observed.

8. The MCA also recommends that the atmosphere of cargo spaces with such oils are continuously monitored during the discharge process for the presence of CO if it is essential for personnel to be within that space. The temperature of the cargo should also be monitored closely. This is particularly important during the closing stages of the cargo discharge operation.

9. Carbon Monoxide is toxic by inhalation and can cause serious damage to health by prolonged exposure. Hence the 8 hour exposure limit for personnel to CO concentrations is 30 parts per million, though for short term exposure not exceeding 15 minutes, concentrations of up to 200 parts per million can be allowed.

10. Monitoring equipment should be capable of achieving the above degree of accuracy.

Environmental Quality Branch
Maritime and Coastguard Agency
Spring Place
105 Commercial Road
Southampton SO15 1EG

Tel: 02380 329100
Fax: 02380 329204

eRef: MS 116/032/0005

ly 2002

Department for

Transport

*An executive agency of the
Department for Transport*

Safer Lives, Safer Ships, Cleaner Seas

MARINE GUIDANCE NOTE

MGN 86 (M)

Maritime and Coastguard Agency

RECOMMENDATIONS ON THE SAFE USE OF PESTICIDES IN SHIPS

Notice to operators, shipowners, charterers, masters, agents, port and harbour authorities, shippers, container and vehicle packers, cargo terminal operators, fumigators, fumigant and pesticide manufacturers and all persons responsible for the unloading of freight containers

(This notice takes immediate effect)

Summary

The purpose of this guidance note is to advise on:

(1) the importance of safe and proper procedures when pesticides are used on board ships;

(2) the appropriate application of the IMO Recommendations on the Safe Use of Pesticides in Ships both to cargo and to cargo spaces; and

(3) to indicate the likely application of other related requirements or guidance which would be applicable to the use of, handling or transport of pesticides.

---

1.   In accordance with the Merchant Shipping (Carriage of Cargoes) Regulations 1997[1], where pesticides are used in the cargo spaces of ships prior to, during, or following a voyage, the IMO publication "RECOMMENDATIONS ON THE SAFE USE OF PESTICIDES IN SHIPS" (1996 Edition, IMO267E), available from IMO, Publications Section, 4 Albert Embankment, London SE1 VSR where relevant thereto shall be complied with. The contents of this publication are also incorporated into the Supplement to the International Maritime Dangerous Goods (IMDG) Code. The use of pesticides includes the fumigation of cargo spaces and of cargo, in port, or in-transit, and any part of the ship so affected by their use, as contained in the Recommendations.

2.   The Maritime and Coastguard Agency, in conjunction with the Ministry of Agriculture, [1]Fisheries and Food, the Scottish Office, Agriculture, Environment and

---

[1] S.I. 1997/No.I9 as amended

Fisheries Department and the Health and Safety Executive, considers that it is essential that adequate precautions are taken by all those responsible for the commissioning of pest control on board ships. MCA strongly recommends observance of all the provisions contained in the Recommendations, but the necessity for the master and crew to cooperate with shore-based fumigation personnel in compliance with other safety requirements should be recognised. In the United Kingdom the Health and Safety Executive (HSE) is the relevant shore-based authority.

3.   Mandatory requirements cover the conditions for preparation and carriage of cargo transport units under fumigation. These are classified as Class 9 dangerous goods with the proper shipping name "CARGO TRANSPORT UNIT UNDER FUMIGATION" in the International Maritime Dangerous Goods (IMDG) Code, ("cargo transport unit" being any freight container or vehicle shipped under fumigation). The Merchant Shipping (Dangerous Goods and Marine Pollutants) Regulations 1997 require compliance with the IMDG Code for packaged dangerous goods for aspects such as declaration, stowage, segregation, marking, labelling and the display of a fumigation warning sign.

4.   Pesticides, when not in use and carried as cargo may also be subject to the Regulations specified in paragraph 3 above and the IMDG Code.

5.   The Recommendations regarding fumigation practice were written as a result of consultations with experts on pest control, pesticide safety and ship operation.

6.   In one case, failure to comply with the recommended procedures caused a number of people to be hospitalised after exposure to phosphine gas generated in a cargo of grain fumigated with Aluminium Phosphide during the sea passage. The fumigant tablets were not fully decomposed and, hence, the fumigation process was not fully completed before the vessel arrived at the discharge port. There have also been a number of other incidents involving containerised cargoes arriving under fumigation at United Kingdom ports with no accompanying documentation on the ship or at the port of discharge regarding the nature of the cargo.

7.   Merchant Shipping Notice MSN 1718 should be referred to for the statutory requirements on the safe use of pesticides (including fumigants), in cargo spaces on board ships when they are loaded or intended to be loaded with cargo. Although extensively referred to in these requirements, the scope and application of the IMO Recommendations is generally wider, providing, for example, guidance on the disinfestation of food stores, galleys and crew and passenger accommodation.

8.   As pesticides are hazardous substances their handling and application and exposure to them are subject to regulations affecting the health and safety of workers at work. For further information other related documents should be

referred to, e.g. Chapter 27 of the "Code of Safe Working Practices for Merchant Seamen"[2] and the Health and Safety Executive Approved Code of Practice (Control of Substances Hazardous to Health in Fumigation Operations"[3].

MSASD
Maritime and Coastguard Agency
Spring Place
Southampton SO15 1EG

Tel: 02380 329 184
Fax: 02380 329 204

File reference: MS 116_31_028
August 1998

An excutive agency of the Department of the Enviroment, Transport and the Regions

[2] *Available from The Stationery Office ISBN 0 11 5518363*
[3] *HSE Books ACOP L86 and also Guidance note on Fumigation CS22.*

MARINE GUIDANCE NOTE

MGN 245 (M)

Maritime and Coastguard Agency

Inspection of Shell Loading Doors on Ro Ro Ferries

Notice to: Ship Owners, Ship Builders, Certifying Authorities, Surveyors, Masters and Ships Officers.

Summary

This Guidance Note draws attention to the importance of crewmembers on-board Roll-on Roll-off ferries being aware of the position of the collision bulkhead and the need for it be kept fully intact whenever the ferry is at sea.

Key Points:

- Monthly inspections of shell loading doors

- Additional inspections immediately after every voyage where heavy weather has been encountered

- Notice boards drawing attention to the importance of the extended portion of the collision bulkhead and the need for it to be kept fully intact at sea

- The need for the extended portion of the collision bulkhead to be readily recognisable by crewmembers

1. Background

1.1 Following an incident, which occurred when a Roll-on Roll-off ferry encountered heavy weather whilst crossing the English Channel, damage was sustained to the shell loading door (bow visor). As a result, an investigation was carried out by the Marine Accident Investigation Branch (MAIB). The subsequent MAIB Report 1/8/18 was published and identified a number of recommendations.

1.2 This Guidance Note is intended to promulgate these recommendations to the relevant parties.

2. Collision Bulkheads

2.1 Due to their design and operations, certain vessels are required to have a collision bulkhead. This is a vertical bulkhead, of watertight construction, which extends from the keel to the bulkhead deck (ie usually the lower vehicle deck on a Ro Ro ferry). It has to be located within strictly defined limits (e.g. not less than 5% of the length of the ship abaft the forward perpendicular). Its purpose is to give protection to the main body of the ship in the event of the fore end being breached due to collision or contact damage.

2.2   In addition, on ships which have a forward superstructure, for example the main vehicle space on a Ro Ro passenger ferry, the collision bulkhead may be required to be extended weathertight to the next deck above. This extension need not be fitted directly over the bulkhead below, provided it is not less than 5% of the length of the ship from the forward perpendicular.

2.3   Where an extension of the collision bulkhead is required, it is of vital importance to the Ro Ro passenger ferry. Primarily, it acts as a barrier to the ingress of sea water onto the vehicle decks should the fore end of the ship ever become breached due to collision or contact damage. In addition, it acts as a barrier to the ingress of sea water should the bow visor (or bow door) ever fail to function properly.

3.   Crew Awareness

3.1   The MAIB investigation demonstrated the "vital importance which the extended portion of the collision bulkhead can play in the overall safety of Ro Ro passenger ferries against the ingress of sea water." However the investigation also discovered that "only those crew with a very detailed knowledge of the ship's construction were likely to know of the exact location of the extended portion of the collision bulkhead. Moreover the Inspector was left with the impression that few of the ship's crew fully appreciated the importance the collision bulkhead plays in the overall safety of the ship. A situation which probably applies on most Ro Ro ferries."

4.   Recommendations

4.1   The recommendations made by the MAIB have been fully accepted by the Maritime & Coastguard Agency. These are produced in the following paragraphs.

4.2   All owners and managers of Ro Ro passenger ferries should arrange for:-

- shell loading doors (e.g. bow visors and hinged bow and stern doors), which are required to be weathertight and fitted in their ferries, to be carefully inspected on a monthly basis and also after every voyage where heavy weather has been experienced,

- Any damage found to be quickly and effectively repaired.

- Records of such inspections to be retained for at least 12 months.

- The Maritime & Coastguard Agency to be promptly notified whenever an inspection reveals damage which could lead to the weathertight integrity being compromised.

4.3   All such Ro Ro passenger ferries should have a notice board, placed in a suitable and prominent position on or near the bulkhead, which draws attention to the importance of the extension to the collision bulkhead and the need for it to be kept fully intact whenever the ferry is at sea.

4.4   The extended portion of the collision bulkhead on all Ro Ro passenger ferries, especially when the layout is complicated, is to be readily recognisable to crew members, by special marking or painting, by use of diagrammatic sketches or by some other effective means.

5. Owners and managers should take due account of this guidance and ensure adequate record keeping and training of ship staff in accordance with the Safety Management System.

Survey Branch,
105 Commercial Road
Southampton SO15 1EG

Telephone: 023 80 329220
Fax: 023 80 329104
Internet: http://www.mcga.gov.uk

File Ref: MS008-008-1336

September 2002

Safer Lives, Safer Ships, Cleaner Seas

Department for

Transport

MARINE GUIDANCE NOTE

MGN 284 (M+F)

Maritime and Coastguard Agency

RECOMMENDATIONS FOR SHIPS CARRYING FUMIGATED BULK CARGOES

Notice to operators, shipowners, charterers, masters, agents, port and harbour authorities, shippers, bulk terminal operators, fumigators, fumigant manufacturers and all persons responsible for fumigating bulk cargos.

This MGN should be read in conjunction with MSN 1718, MGN 86 and the Merchant Shinning (Carriage of Cargoes) Regulations 1997 (as amended)

Summary

This guidance note advises on:

(1) the importance of safe and proper procedures when fumigants are used in bulk cargoes on board ships;

(2) the appropriate application of the IMO Recommendations on the Safe Use of Pesticides in ships carrying fumigated bulk cargoes; and

(3) the likely application of other related requirements or guidance that would be applicable to ships carrying fumigated bulk cargoes.

1.0 Introduction/Background

1.1 This MGN has been produced to bring to the attention of ship's masters, owners, agents and port or terminal operators the dangers involved in the transportation and discharged of fumigated solid bulk cargoes.

2.0 Main points

IMO at DSC/Circ11 (available at the IMO website: http://www.imo.org) highlights the following points:

2.1 There may be an incorrect assumption that the concentration of the toxic fumigant in the holds and access ways of the ship is sufficiently low to avoid safety and health risks to ship and shore personnel or enforcement officers when the ship arrives in the port of discharge;

2.2 There are reported incidents where employees have been exposed to the fumigant, usually phosphine, causing health problems; and

2.3 Ships containing bulk cargo under fumigation, unlike in container transport units (CTUs), have no requirement to be labelled as such, and therefore may not be visibly recognised as a potential health and safety risk. It should be noted that there is a requirement in the 'Code of Safe Practice for Merchant Seamen' to ensure that fumigation warning signs are conspicuously displayed on cargo units or spaces under fumigation.

3.0   The safe use of pesticides on ships

3.1.   The International Convention for the Safety of Life at Sea (SOLAS) regulation VI/4, requires that appropriate precautions are taken in the use of pesticides in ships, in particular for the purposes of fumigation.

3.2   The Merchant Shipping (Carriage of Cargoes) Regulations 1997 require that where pesticides are used in the cargo spaces of ships prior to, or following a voyage, the IMO publication *Recommendations on the Safe Use of Pesticides in Ships* (2002 Edition) must be complied with. These regulations define 'the use of pesticides' to include the fumigation of cargo spaces and of cargo, in port, or in transit, and in any part of the ship or cargo so affected as a consequence of their application or use, as referred to in the 'Recommendations'.

3.3   To ensure compliance with the *Recommendations* detailed in 3.2 above all ships proceeding to a port within the United Kingdom, carrying solid bulk cargoes under fumigation, even if ventilation of the cargo has taken place during the voyage, must prior to arrival and in general not less than 24 hours in advance, inform either the port authority or terminal operator of the port or bulk terminal of destination that the bulk cargo has been fumigated.

This information must be provided by either the ship's master, owner or the agent.

3.4   In cases where the presence of personnel in cargo spaces is required to ensure that fumigation tablets have fully decomposed before arrival at the discharge port, it is important that the Ship's master ensures that adequate respiratory protection (e.g. self contained compressed air breathing apparatus) is worn until all fumigation residues have been removed and the spaces have been thoroughly ventilated.

3.5   On arrival at any port within the United Kingdom where fumigated bulk cargo is to be discharged the master must establish the requirements of the port or bulk terminal regarding the handling of fumigated cargoes before any cargo is discharged. Before entry of fumigated cargo spaces, trained personnel from a fumigation company or other competent persons, wearing respiratory protection, must carry out careful monitoring of the spaces to ensure the safety of personnel. The monitoring values must be entered in the ships log book. The fumigation is not complete until the holds and cargo have been ventilated and tested and a certificate issued by a competent person stating that the cargo and holds are free from harmful concentrations of gas,

3.6   When the ship is found to be free of fumigants and certified as such, all warning signs should be removed. Any action in this respect should be recorded in the ship's log book

3.7   The precautions and procedures detailed in the 'Code of Safe Working Practices for Merchant Seamen' with regard to the entering of enclosed spaces should be taken in account.

3.8   The Merchant Shipping (International Safety Management (ISM) Code) Regulations 1998 require ships to develop plans for key shipboard operations concerning the safety of the ship and the prevention of pollution. These plans must include safety procedures for fumigation if the ship is likely to carry solid bulk cargo that may require fumigation.

4.0   Further Information

Further information on the contents of this MGN can be obtained from colin.thomas@mcga.gov.uk (or the address at the end of this Notice)

Environmental Quality Branch
Maritime and Coastguard Agency
Spring Place
105 Commercial Road
S015 1EG
Telephone: 023 8032 9402
Fax: 023 8032 9204
E-Mail: colin.thomas@mcga.gov.uk

General Enquiries: 24 Hour Info Line
                    infoline@mcga.gov.uk
                    0870 600 6505
MCA Website Address: Internet:
http://www.mcga.gov.uk
File Ref: MS/41/16/14
Published: March 2005
© Crown Copyright 2005

Safer Lives, Safer Ships, Cleaner Seas

Department for

Transport

The MCA is an executive agency of the Department for Transport

Maritime and Coastguard Agency

MARINE GUIDANCE NOTE

MGN 144 (M)

The Merchant Shipping (Additional Safety Measures for Bulk Carriers) Regulations 1999 (SI 1999/1644)

Notice to Surveyors, Shipowners, Masters, Bulk Cargo Shippers and Terminal operators

Summary

This MGN draws attention to the Merchant Shipping (Additional Safety Measures for Bulk Carriers) Regulations 1999 which came into force on 1st July 1999.

Key Points:

- These Regulations implement SOLAS Chapter XII to enhance the structural safety and resistance to flooding of bulk carriers.

- This Marine Guidance Note gives advice for the guidance of surveyors on the interpretation and application of these regulations.

INTRODUCTION

1. These regulations enact SOLAS Chapter XII adopted during the 1997 SOLAS Conference with effect from 1st July 1999. They relate to bulk carriers of 150m in length and upwards, carrying high density dry bulk cargoes, and introduce standards for damage stability and flotation, structure of bulkheads and double bottoms, overall longitudinal strength in the flooded state, hold loading, cargo density declarations, and provision of a loading instrument. The regulations also define how compliance with the requirements should be documented.

2. For new ships, the regulations require the checking of the structure and stability of the vessel with any hold flooded in all load conditions. The requirements are applicable to new ships carrying high density cargoes of over 1000 kg/m3. Structural standards

for bulkheads, double bottoms and longitudinal strength are defined by IACS Unified Requirements and are referenced in an IMO Conference Resolution.

3. The requirements are also retrospectively applied to existing vessels. Research has shown that the majority of bulk carrier incidents affect those over 15 years old, carrying high density cargoes with alternate hold loading, and 40–50% involve the forward hold. There is a long phase-in period for existing vessels, whereby those over 15 years of age are checked and modified if required first, and the youngest vessels have until they are 17 years old to comply. The requirements apply to existing ships carrying cargoes with density of 1780 kg/m3 or over, as this was considered the point at which alternate hold loading becomes viable. Structural standards are specified in detail in a separate IMO Conference

Resolution which incorporates in full the relevant IACS Unified Requirements. These only apply in the case of flooding of the forward hold, and because of this there is no special additional requirement for overall longitudinal strength in the flooded condition.

4. For ease of interpretation and correlation with international regulations, this Marine Guidance Note is drafted in terms of the SOLAS Regulations and applicable IACS standards. In this respect it should be noted that the IACS Unified Requirements are incorporated into the classification rules of each IACS member society.

5. The following table relates these to the UK regulations numbers

SOLAS Chapter XII Regulation	Topic	UK Bulk Carriers Regulation	IACS Standard
1	Definitions	2	
2	Application	3	
-	Enhanced surveys of bulk carriers	4	URZ10.2 refers
3	Implementation Schedule`	5	(URS23 refers)
4.1	Damage stability - new ships	6(1)	
4.2	Damage stability - existing ships	6(2)	
5	Structural strength - new ships	7	URS17, 18, 20
6	Structural strength - existing ships	8	URS19, 22
6.3	Loading restrictions as alternative to structural modifications - existing ships	8(3)	
7	Completion of enhanced periodical survey - existing ships over 10 years old	9	
8	Information on compliance	10	
9	Relaxation of stability and structural requirements - existing ships with insufficient watertight bulkheads	14	(URS24 refers)
10	Cargo density declaration	11	
11	Loading instrument	12	Rec. No. 48

Regulation XII/2 - Application

6.   The Regulations apply only to those bulk carriers as defined in Conference Resolution 6 of the 1997 SOLAS Conference, which is also in line with the interpretation adopted for ISM Code compliance. They apply to -

    a.   bulk carriers with the traditional structural configuration of single deck, upper wing tanks and lower hopper tanks in cargo areas;

    b.   ore carriers with two longitudinal bulkheads and double bottom in cargo areas, carrying ore cargoes in the centre holds only;

    c.   combination carriers, ie tankers also able to carry dry cargo in bulk.

7.   Other ship configurations are excluded from the Regulations, even if the ship is carrying solid bulk cargoes. Most of the individual regulations apply only to bulk carriers, as defined, of single side skin construction and of 150m in length and upwards. Ore carriers are double side skin by definition and are therefore exempt from most regulations.

8.   A number of bulk carriers are constructed of mixed construction, with double side skins throughout most of the cargo area (for ease of cargo handling) but single side skin construction in the forward hold (for ease of construction). These come under the SOLAS definition of "bulk carrier of single side skin construction" as there is "a hold bounded by the side shell" and therefore Chapter XII, if interpreted literally, would require the double skinned cargo holds of new ships to meet the structural requirements intended by SOLAS

Regulations XII/4 and 6 for single skin holds.

9.   The term "bulk carrier of single side skin construction" was therefore clarified by IMO in Annex 1 to Resolution MSC89/71, which is attached to this Marine Guidance Note at Appendix B and which should be used as an interpretation of this term.

10.   Evidence was submitted to IMO's Maritime Safety Committee's 71st session in May 1999 indicating that ships carrying heavy break bulk cargoes, such as steel components, rail tracks, etc may be faced with similar problems as bulk carriers, because of the very high permeability of the cargo spaces when fully loaded. However the Committee agreed to await the results of further research on the matter before deciding whether SOLAS Chapter XII should also apply to ships carrying these cargoes.

Surveys of Bulk Carriers

11.   The IMO Enhanced Survey Programme was made mandatory from 1st January 1996 for bulk carriers and oil tankers by SOLAS Chapter XI, and bulk carriers are not permitted by SOLAS Chapter XII to carry dense cargoes unless they have been surveyed in accordance with the IMO Guidelines (Resolution A.744(18), as updated by Resolution 2 of the 1997 SOLAS Conference).

12.   95% of bulk carriers are classed with IACS member societies which have already enacted these requirements within their own rules. However, there remains a need in the UK Regulations to stipulate this requirement at regulation 5, primarily to ensure compliance by the remaining 5%.

Regulations XII/3 and XII/7 - Implementation Schedule

13.   The regulations apply, in full, to all new ships, ie those whose keels are laid on or after 1st July 1999. Most bulk carriers are classed with IACS member classification societies which have implemented the relevant structural and stability requirements for their own ships since 1st July 1998.

14.   For an existing ship over 15 years of age, regulations XII/4 and 6 (dealing with structure and damage stability) are effective at the date of the first periodical survey after 1st July 1999; for ships over 20 years of age this would apply from the date of the first intermediate or periodical survey, but in either case it should be completed by 1 July 2002. If a vessel underwent a survey immediately prior to 1st July 1999 then implementation of the regulations might be delayed by up to three years. This is not the intention of the regulations and on IACS' ships early completion of an intermediate or special survey due after 1st July 1998 to postpone compliance is not allowed by IACS Unified Requirement S23 para. 1(b). For non-IACS ships the effective date would be 1st July 1999.

15.   No bulk carrier over ten years old may carry a high density bulk cargo unless she has undergone either a periodical survey or a survey of her cargo holds to an equivalent extent, as required by regulation XII/7.

16.   Regulation XII/9 permits exemptions to certain ships that cannot comply with regulation XII/4.2 on condition that they are subject to additional surveys, fitted with bilge alarms and furnished with additional information. Although regulation XII/9 mentions no specific implementation date it is not expected that such ships should comply with these alternative provisions before the date on which they would have had to comply with regulation 4.2.

17.   Enhanced surveys were required for bulk carriers from 1st January 1996, and additional requirements for these surveys were introduced by Resolution 2 of the 1997 SOLAS Conference. However many ships started these surveys before that date, and Resolution 7 accepts such surveys for the purposes of compliance with these regulations, provided the surveys were undertaken before 1st January 1996.

18.   An aide-memoir in the form of a table indicating, for age of ship, the regulations with which she has to comply, is attached at Appendix A for information of Port State Control Officers (PSCOs).

Regulation XII/4 - Damage Stability Requirements

19.   The damage stability standards referred to in SOLAS Chapter XII are those of the "Regulation equivalent to regulation 27 of the International Convention of Load Lines, 1966" adopted by Resolution A.320(IX) on 12 November 1975, as amended by Resolution A.514(13) on 17 November 1983. The consolidated text of these resolutions is included in the UK Regulations at regulation 6(3) for completeness and is updated to remove ambiguity in the context of bulk carriers

20.   Bulk carriers with B-60 or B-100 freeboards are subject to an equivalent damage survivability check under the

existing 1966 International Convention on Load Lines, and existing ships of such types are deemed to comply with the requirements. Foreign flag ships may, instead, have been assigned a reduced freeboard in compliance with either Resolution A.320(IX)/Resolution A.514(13) or Regulation 27(8) of Annex B of the 1988 Protocol to the International Convention of Load Lines, 1966. Either of these may also be accepted as complying with the required standards.

21.   These are deterministic standards which seek to ensure that the ship can withstand a given level of damage within a statutory safety margin. SOLAS II-1/25-1 imposes a probabilistic standard of survivability, which requires the vessel to achieve an index of survival based on the probability of collision damage extent and load condition. This is not permitted as an equivalent to the deterministic damage requirements. Conversely, the deterministic standards above may be accepted as an alternative to the probabilistic requirements, as noted in the footnote to Regulation II 1/25-1.1.

Regulations XII/5 and 6 - Structural requirements

22.   The structure of new bulk carriers, designed to carry solid bulk cargoes having a density of 1000kg/m³ or greater, is required to comply with the IACS Unified Requirements S7, S18 and S20, as defined in Conference Resolution 3 of the 1997 SOLAS Conference. The Conference is aware of the difficulty of applying 'S' standards to IMO regulations, as these standards are "live" documents and could be amended by IACS without

recourse to IMO. However it was considered that as the majority of bulk carriers would be IACS-classed anyway there would be few problems in using the IACS standards for these vessels.

23.   The IACS standards UR S19 (Evaluation of Scantlings of the transverse watertight corrugated bulkhead between cargo holds Nos. 1 and 2, with cargo hold No. 1 flooded) and UR S22 (Evaluation of Allowable Hold Loading of Cargo Hold No. 1 with Cargo Hold No. 1 Flooded) apply retrospectively to existing single side skin bulk carriers. This time, in order to avoid the situation identified above, where a future IACS update would retrospectively affect existing ships without recourse to IMO, the technical content of these IACS URs is incorporated as Annexes 1 and 2 of Conference Resolution 4. This "freezes" the standard but still allows IMO to update it in future with a further IMO Resolution.

24.   The retrospective standards only apply to existing bulk carriers carrying cargoes of density 1780kg/m3 or greater. High density cargoes are seen as being more hazardous than the same total weight of a lower density cargo because of the large empty volumes left in cargo holds. This permits a greater weight of sea-water to enter in the event of a breach of the hull envelope, leading to possible hull or bulkhead failure and/ or loss of stability.

25.   Many existing ships will require strengthening of their double bottom and/or transverse bulkhead structure in way of the forward hold in order to comply with these standards. Regulation XII/6.3 permits, as an alternative, that

the ship accepts limitations on either the total deadweight loaded or on cargo distribution restrictions such as avoiding alternate hold loading. These alternatives must be documented as at regulation XII/8. They are only applicable, though, when loading cargo with a density greater than 1780 kg/m³.

Regulation XII/9 - Ships unable to comply with the hold flooding requirements

26.   Regulation XII/9 anticipates that a number of existing bulk carriers of over 150m will be unable to comply with the flooding requirements of regulation 4.2. These might be four hold ships, where flooding of the forward hold represents an excessive loss of buoyancy, or ships such as selfdischarging cement carriers with hoppers and discharge conveyors running through their bulkheads, rendering them non-watertight and again unable to comply.

27.   Regulation XII/9 therefore permits exemption from the stability and structural standards subject to annual enhanced inspections for the forward hold, fitting of bilge well alarms in all cargo holds, and provision of additional information on emergency procedures. The exemption is not permitted for new ships. Regulation 9.2 calls for high level alarms to be fitted in bilge wells, but it is possible that this could be triggered by relatively small quantities of water and may not give indication of catastrophic flooding. Ship owners are therefore strongly recommended to comply with IACS' URS24 providing for "high high" level alarms in such ships.

28.   Chapter XII of SOLAS refers to Administrations permitting "relaxations" rather than granting "exemptions".

The term "exemption" has been used in regulation 14 of the UK regulations so as to ensure that UK flag ships will have the benefit of a formal document demonstrating compliance to exhibit to PSCOs when in foreign ports.

29.   SOLAS Chapter XII defines no formal documentation to demonstrate that this relaxation has been permitted in respect of a ship. UK PSCOs may therefore find some difficulty in obtaining confirmation that such relaxation has been officially permitted.

30.   IMO Resolution MSC79(70) expresses concern that owners might modify existing watertight bulkheads on a bulk carrier that would otherwise have to comply with regulations XII/4.2 and 6, so as to render the bulkheads non-watertight, and it is emphasised that this regulation is only applicable to ships originally constructed in this manner.

31.   Clearly any bulk carrier modified in this way would not also be able to continue to benefit from a B-60 Freeboard and it is therefore not clear that this method would be of value to many bulk carrier owners, but it may occur with certain ships of specialist design.

Regulation XII/8 - Documentation of Compliance

32.   There is currently no formal certification in place to indicate compliance with these standards. IMO Resolution MSC79(70) urges Administrations to ensure that bulk carriers to which these regulations apply are clearly identified as such, either on the ISM Safety Management Certificate or in the Cargo Loading Manual. In the longer term the Cargo Ship Safety Construction, Safety

Equipment and Safety Certificates will be amended to include "bulk carrier" as one of the recognised ship types but this can only take place after the 1988 SOLAS Protocol comes into effect on 3 February 2000.

33.   The Cargo Loading Manual, required by SOLAS Regulation VI-7.2 from 1 July 1998 (as enacted in the UK by regulation 10(2) of the Merchant Shipping (Carriage of Cargoes) Regulations 1999, should be endorsed by the Certifying Authority to indicate which of the SOLAS regulations identified in the table at Appendix A are complied with.

34.   Regulation XII/8.3 requires a triangle, of side 500mm in length, painted in a contrasting colour with its apex 300mm below the deck line, to be marked on the side shell of the ship when compliance with regulation XII/6.2 involves imposition of loading/operating restrictions as described in regulation XII/6.3. Recognising that strict implementation of regulation XII/8.3 would result in every bulk carrier constructed before 1 July 1999 being so marked, and as this was not the intention of the regulation, IMO has published interpretations to be followed when determining if triangle marks are required as Annex 2 to IMO Resolution MSC89(71) which is attached to this Marine Guidance Note at Appendix B.

Regulation XII/10 – Density declaration and verification

35.   The shipper is required to declare the density of the cargo being carried, in addition to the other information required by SOLAS Regulation VI/2.2, as implemented in the UK by regulation 4(1) of the Merchant Shipping (Carriage of Cargoes) Regulations 1999. This is not strictly a safety requirement, as the safety of the vessel is more governed by the actual weight loaded into each hold, but it is important to verify compliance with the 1780 kg/m3 limit for existing ships. Therefore any cargo declared to have a density in the range of 1250 kg/m3 to 1780 kg/m3 must have its density verified by an accredited testing organisation.

36.   This cargo density verification is clearly only of relevance to those existing ships not permitted to carry high density cargoes. IMO Resolution MSC79(70) clarifies that for bulk carriers of 150m in length and upwards of single side skin construction constructed before 1st July 1999, any cargo carried on or after the implementation date specified in regulation XII/3 and declared to have a density within the range of 1250 to 1780 kg/m3 shall have its density verified by an accredited testing organisation, unless such bulk carriers comply with all the relevant requirements of the Regulations applicable to the carriage of solid bulk cargoes having a density of 1780 kg/m3 andover.

37.   In verifying the density of solid bulk cargoes reference may be made to MSC Circular 908 dated 9 June 1998 on a Uniform Method of the measurement of the bulk density of bulk cargoes. This Circular is also attached to this Marine Guidance Note at Appendix C. This Circular does not make clear, however, the means to ensure that a representative sample is taken for density measurement, and therefore

reference should be made to IMO's Code of Safe Practice for Solid Bulk Cargoes (the BC Code), in particular Section 1 para. 1.10, Section 4.3 and Annex D.

Regulation 11 - Loading Instrument

38. This refers to Resolution 5 of the 1997 SOLAS Conference, which in turn refers to IACS Recommendation No. 48 for ships not yet fitted with a loading instrument.

39. Loading instruments previously fitted to bulk carriers should have been approved in accordance with the standards of a recognised organisation. The Maritime and Coastguard Agency

Load Line and Cargo Ship Safety Branch
Spring Place
Commercial Road
Southampton SO15 1EG

Tel: 023 8032 9100
Fax: 023 8032 9161

April 2000
[MS10/25/44]

DETI
ENVIRONMENT
TRANSPORT
REGIONS

An excutive agency of the Department of Enviroment, Transport and the Region.

	New Ships (SSSC, >150 m, >1000 kg/m³) (constructed on or after 1 July 1999)	Existing Ships (SSSC, >150 m, >1780 kg/m³) — Implementation Schedule		
		<15 years old (constructed 2 July 84 - 30 June 99)	15-20 years old (constructed 2 July 79 - 1 July 84)	20 years old and over (constructed on or before 1 July 79)
3 (Implementation Schedule)				
4 (Damage Stability)	Applies; Loading manual to be endorsed;	Applies at 1st periodical survey after age 15 years, but not later than age 17 years; Loading manual to be endorsed	Applies at 1st periodical survey after 1/7/99, but not later than 1/7/02; Loading manual to be endorsed	Applies at 1st intermediate or periodical survey after 1/7/99, but not later than 1/7/02; Loading manual to be endorsed
5 (Structural Strength)	Applies; Loading manual to be endorsed;	N/A		
6 (Structural Strength)	N/A	Applies at 1st periodical survey after age 15 years, but not later than age 17 years; Loading manual to be endorsed	Applies at 1st periodical survey after 1/7/99, but not later than 1/7/02; Loading manual to be endorsed	Applies at 1st intermediate or periodical survey after 1/7/99, but not later than 1/7/02; Loading manual to be endorsed
6.3 (Loading restrictions instead of structural mods)	N/A	Applies from date that Regulation 6 would have applied; Loading manual to be endorsed and triangle mark to be applied to ship's side; Loading manual to detail loading and operational restrictions, or restrictions on loading cargoes of density > 1780 kg/m³, to be stated.		
7 (Enhanced Surveys)	N/A	Applies to any ship over 10 years of age carrying a cargo of density > 1780 kg/m³		
8 (Information on Compliance)	Applies	Applies at 1st periodical survey after age 15 years, but not later than age 17 years	Applies at 1st periodical survey after 1/7/99, but not later than 1/7/02	Applies at 1st intermediate or periodical survey after 1/7/99, but not later than 1/7/02
9 (Ships unable to comply with Reg. 4.2)	N/A	Applies from date that Regulation 4 would have applied; Loading manual to be endorsed.		
10.1 (Cargo Density Declaration)		Applies from 1 July 1999 to all bulk cargoes loaded on all bulk carriers.		
10.2 (Verification of Density)	N/A	Applies to cargoes 1250 kg/m³-1780 kg/m³ carried on ships not permitted (under 6.3) to carry cargoes over 1780 kg/m³, from date that Regulation 6 would have applied.		
11 (Loading Instrument)	Applies to all bulk carriers >150 m	Applies to all bulk carriers >150 m at 1st intermediate or periodical survey after 1 July 1999		

APPENDIX B

MSC 71/23/.Add. 1

ANNEX 1

INTERPRETATION OF THE TERM "BULK CARRIER OF SINGLE SIDE SKIN CONSTRUCTION"

1. "Bulk carrier of single side skin construction" means a bulk carrier where one or more cargo holds are bound by the side shell only or by two watertight boundaries, one of which is the side shell, which are less than 760 mm apart in bulk carriers constructed before 1 January 2000 and less than 1,000 mm a part in bulk carriers constructed on or after 1 January 2000. The distance between the watertight boundaries is to be measured perpendicular to the side shell.

2. The above interpretation should be applied as follows:

   .1 in bulk carriers with single side skin construction in the foremost cargo hold, constructed before 1 July 1999, regulations XII/4.2 and 6 should be applied in accordance with the implementation schedule required by regulation XII/3; and

   .2 in bulk carriers constructed on or after 1 July 1999, the requirements for damage stability under regulation XII/4.1 and structural integrity under regulation X11/5 should be complied with in respect of cargo holds with single side skin construction.

ANNEX 2

INTERPRETATION OF THE REQUIREMENT FOR CERTAIN BULK CARRIERS TO BE PERMANENTLY MARKED ON THE SIDE SHELL WITH A TRIANGLE

SOLAS regulation XII/8.3 requires a triangle to be marked on the side shell of the ship when compliance with regulation XII/6.2 involves imposition of loading/operating restrictions as described in regulation XII/6.3. Such operating restrictions only need to be imposed for solid bulk cargoes having a density of 1,780 kg/m^3 and above, and apply at all times when solid bulk cargoes having a density of 1,780 kg/m^3 and above are carried. The following interpretations should be followed when determining if triangle marks are required:

1. When a ship's loading booklet restricts the ship to carry solid bulk cargoes having a density of less than 1,780 kg/m3, a triangle mark is not required, provided that all reference to carriage of solid bulk cargoes having a density. of 1,780 kg/m^3 and above are removed from the loading booklet. The loading booklet is to clearly specify that the ship is prohibited from carrying solid bulk cargoes having a density of 1,780 kg/m3 and above.

2. When a ship's deadweight is restricted, but the load line assignment permits deeper draughts

and operating restrictions in the form of draught or deadweight limits are imposed on the ship to obtain compliance with the requirements, the loading booklet is to clearly specify the operating restrictions and a triangle is to be permanently marked on the ship's sides. If the ship's load line and loading booklet are revised to limit the ship's draught at all times, operating restrictions and the triangle marks are not required.

3. Where restrictions, other than a general restriction to homogeneous loading, are imposed on the distribution of cargo in the two foremost cargo holds as a condition of compliance, then the loading booklet is to clearly specify the applicable operating restrictions and a triangle is to be permanently marked on the ship's sides.

4. Where restrictions are imposed on the maximum mass of packaged cargoes to be carried in the foremost cargo hold as a condition of compliance with the Standards for the evaluation of allowable hold loading of the foremost cargo hold, as contained in annex 2 to 1997 SOLAS Conference resolution 4, the loading booklet is to clearly state these limits, but the triangle marks are not required.

5. Where a homogeneous distribution of cargo in the two foremost cargo holds is required as a condition of compliance, then the loading booklet is to clearly specify the applicable operating restrictions and a triangle is to be permanently marked on the ship's sides.

ANNEX 6

RESOLUTION MSC.89(71)

(adopted on -28 May 1999)

INTERPRETATION OF THE PROVISIONS OF SOLAS CHAPTER XII ON ADDITIONAL SAFETY MEASURES FOR BULK CARRIERS

THE MARITIME SAFETY COMMITTEE,

RECALLING Article 28(b) of the Convention on the International Maritime Organization concerning the functions of the Committee,

NOTING that the 1997 SOLAS Conference adopted chapter XII of the International Convention for the Safety of Life at Sea (SOLAS), 1974 concerning additional safety measures for bulk carriers.

NOTING FURTHER that SOLAS chapter XII will enter into force on 1 July 1999.

DESIRING to ensure that all Contracting Governments to the 1974 SOLAS Convention implement SOLAS chapter XII in a consistent and uniform manner,

RECOGNIZING, therefore, the need to establish, for that purpose, guidance on applications of, and the interpretation to, the relevant provisions of that chapter, further to that already adopted by, resolution MSC.79(70),

RESPONDING to the request of the 1997 SOLAS Conference, as recorded in Conference resolution thereof, regarding. the term "bulk carrier of single side skin construction",

REALIZING that SOLAS regulation XII/8.3, if applied literally, would require every bulk carrier of 150 m in length and upwards of single side skin construction, carrying solid bulk cargoes having a density of 1,780 kg/m3 and above constructed before 1 July 1999, to be permanently marked on the side shell with a solid triangle, and recognizing that this is clearly not the intention of the regulation.

1. URGES Governments concerned to:

.1 interpret the term "bulk carrier of single side skin construction" defined in regulation XII/1.2 as indicated in Annex 1 to the present resolution; and

.2 interpret the requirement for certain bulk carriers to be permanently marked on the side shell with a triangle, provided in SOLAS regulation XII/8.3, as indicated in Annex 2 to the present resolution; and

2. INVITES Governments concerned to bring the contents of this resolution to the attention of all parties concerned.

MSC/Circ.908
4 June 1999

UNIFORM METHOD OF MEASUREMENT OF THE DENSITY OF BULK CARGOES

1.   SOLAS regulation XII/10 (Solid bulk cargo density declaration), as adopted by the 1997 SOLAS Conference on Bulk Carrier Safety and interpreted by operative paragraph 4 of resolution MSC 79 (70), requires the shipper, prior to loading bulk cargo on a bulk carrier, to declare the density of the cargo which shall be verified by an accredited testing organization.

2.   The Maritime Safety Committee, at its seventy - first session (19 to 28 May 1999), recognizing the need for a uniform method of density measurement of the bulk cargoes, adopted the performance specification for the measurement of the density of such cargoes set out at annex.

3.   Member Governments are invited to bring this circular to the attention of all parties concerned.

ANNEX

PERFORMANCE SPECIFICATION FOR THE MEASUREMENT OF THE DENSITY OF BULK CARGOES*

1. Scope

1.1   This specification may be used to determine the bulk density of bulk cargoes.

1.2   Bulk density is the weight of solids, air and water per unit volume. It includes the moisture content of the cargo and the voids whether filled with air or water.

1.3   The density should be expressed in kilograms per cubic metre (kg/m^3).

2. Apparatus

2.1   This specification provides for the use of a container of known volume and tare weight.

2.2   The container should be sufficiently rigid to prevent deformation or volume changes occurring during the test. Where the material contains lumps, or will not readily flow into corners, the container should be of cylindrical shape and/or of large size in comparison to the size of lumps. Its capacity must be large enough to contain a representative sample of the cargo for which the density is to be determined.

2.3   The internal surfaces of the container should be smooth with any attachments such as handles being fitted to the exterior.

2.4   Weighing should be done using a weighing instrument certified by an accredited testing organization.

3. Procedure

3.1   A sample that is representative of the particle size, compaction and moisture of the material to be loaded on the ship should be selected.

3.2   The container should be filled with a sample of the material so that it is trimmed level with the top of the container. The material should not be tamped.

3.3   The weight of the filled container should be measured and the tare weight subtracted to obtain the weight of the sample.

3.4   The density of the sample should be calculated by dividing the weight of the bulk material to be loaded by the volume of the container.

4.   Recording results

4.1   The density of the sample should be recorded using the recommended form given in the appendix and made available when requested.

4.2   The result of the density measurement should be signed by a representative of the accredited testing organization.

* Reference is made to paragraph 1.10 - "Representative test sample" and Appendix D - "Laboratory test proce-dures, associated apparatus and standards" of the Code of Safe Practice for Solid Bulk Cargoes (BC Code).

Appendix

RECORD OF DENSITY MEASUREMENT

The density of the cargo has been measured in accordance with the uniform method of density measurement of bulk cargoes described in the annex to MSC/Circ.908 which refers to SOLAS regulation XII/10.

Cargo: (name and relevant reference in the BC Code):

Shipper (name, address, telephone, etc.)

Sample origin (stock pile, ship's hold, etc.)

Date (sampling and density measurement)

Gross weight (GW) (container plus sample)		kg
Tare weight (TW) (container)		kg
Net weight (NW) (sample)	(NW=GW -TW):	kg
Volume (V) (container)		m³
Calculated density (d) of the cargo	(d= NW/V)	kg/m³

Measurement conducted by the accredited testing organization
(Signature, stamp)

Done on   at

MARINE GUIDANCE NOTE

MGN 340 (M)

Maritime and Coastguard Agency

International Maritime Dangerous Goods (IMDG) Code and Cargoes Carried in Cargo Transport Units

Notice to all Ship Owners, Ship Operators and Managers, Masters and Officers of Merchant Ships, Agents, Charterers, Cargo Packers, Cargo Consolidators, Hauliers, Freight Forwarders, Shippers, Consignors, Training Providers, Inspectors of Cargoes, Port Authorities, Terminal Operators, Passengers and others involved in the transport of dangerous goods and other cargoes carried in cargo transport units by sea.

This notice replaces MGN 159

PLEASE NOTE:-

Where this document provides guidance on the law it should not be regarded as definitive. The way the law applies to any particular case can vary according to circumstances - for example, from vessel to vessel and you should consider seeking independent legal advice if you are unsure of your own legal position.

Summary

This Marine Guidance Note gives details on cargoes which are classified as dangerous in accordance with the International Maritime Dangerous Goods (IMDG) Code. It also gives details of other cargoes which may present a risk to the ship, crew, passengers and the environment when carried in cargo transport units (CTUs).

It also:

Provides for and advises on general approvals where these are required or permitted by the IMDG Code.

Advises and gives clarification on the carriage of the cargoes described above to ensure their safe transport whilst facilitating their smooth passage along the transport supply chain.

Assists with the implementation of the IMDG Code.

Advises on future revisions of this MGN.

1. The Merchant Shipping (Dangerous Goods and Marine Pollutants) Regulations 1997 implement the International Maritime Dangerous Goods (IMDG) Code and apply to all United Kingdom ships and all ships in United Kingdom waters.

2. The IMDG Code and its Supplement are directed at everyone involved in the transport of dangerous goods by sea and its provisions affect industries and services involved in the supply chain from manufacturer/consignor to consignee and passengers.

3. Future editions or amendments of the IMDG Code will be announced in a Merchant Shipping Notice. In order to keep up to date with the latest amendments coming from the UN Recommendations on the Transport of Dangerous Goods which is published biennially and provides the source of most of the updating, the IMDG Code will be published on a two yearly cycle. Amendments to the Code will be published electronically on the MCA dangerous goods website, address given on page 4 of this document, shortly after they are adopted by the International Maritime Organization (IMO).

4. Properly planned and maintained training programmes are an essential means of ensuring that those involved in the transport of dangerous goods by sea can demonstrate their compliance with the relevant parts of the IMDG Code and should be commensurate with their responsibilities. Further guidance on training requirements is given in Chapter 1.3 of the IMDG Code.

5. Chapters 1 to 7.8 of the Code refer to approvals, including permits, authorizations or agreements, and certificates and give permission for Competent Authorities to vary Code provisions providing general standards are followed. When this is done and properly authorized by a Competent Authority, Chapter 7.9 of the Code gives assurance that such Approvals will be fully acceptable in other countries. In the United Kingdom, approvals are dealt with on a case by case basis by the MCA. The MCA has issued a small number of General Approvals which are given in the Annex to this notice.

6. The period of validity of ad hoc approvals issued under chapter 1 to 7.8 of the IMDG Code will vary, but the maximum period will not exceed two years from the date of issue in order to align with the issue of new amendments to the IMDG Code. United Kingdom Competent Authority Approvals issued by the MCA that do not state a validity period or that are over 2 years old should not be considered as a valid MCA approval and should immediately be brought to the attention of the MCA for revision.

7. A copy of an MCA approval must either accompany the shipment or, the Dangerous Goods Transport Document must contain details of where the approval is located. Approvals are only valid for transport from the UK to the eventual port of destination and not for any subsequent onward journeys.

8. The MCA issues two types of exemption;

(1) Under SOLAS for the ship

(2) Under Chapter 7.9 of the IMDG Code for the consignor.

The MCA will continue to issue exemptions for vessels engaged in domestic journeys, a domestic voyage being a ferry whose voyage is from one port within UK waters to the same or another port within the UK. Requests for route specific exemptions should be addressed in the first instance to the ferry operator who after consideration, may wish to request a vessel exemption from the MCA.

For vessels engaged on international journeys the issuing of exemptions not mentioned in chapters 1 to 7.8 of the IMDG Code can be in accordance with the following paragraphs and Chapter 7.9 of the IMDG Code.

The IMDG Code, except for Class 7, allows a Competent Authority or Competent Authorities to grant exemptions from specific requirements of the IMDG Code for international voyages in accordance with the following conditions:

- that such provisions are at least as effective and offer an equivalent level of safety as that required by the Code
- acceptance of an exemption authorized under this section by a competent authority not party to it is subject to the discretion of that competent authority.

Accordingly, prior to any shipment covered by the exemption being shipped, the recipient of the exemption must notify other competent authorities concerned.

9.   Competent Authority or Competent Authorities which have taken the initiative with respect to an exemption:

- must send a copy of the exemption to the International Maritime Organization (IMO) which must bring it to the attention of the Contracting Parties to SOLAS

and/or MARPOL, as appropriate. IMO will publish such exemptions on their web site and

- if appropriate, take action to amend the IMDG Code to include the provisions covered by the exemption.

The period of validity of such exemption will not be more than five years from the date of authorization.

A copy of the exemption must accompany each consignment when offered to the carrier for transport under the terms of the exemption. A copy of the exemption or an electronic copy must be maintained on board each ship transporting dangerous goods in accordance with the exemption, as appropriate.

Information on approvals or exemptions which the UK has issued or agreed can be found on the MCA dangerous goods website at http://www.mcga.gov.uk/c4mca/mcga-safety information/mcqa-dangerous goods.htm

10.   Reporting Requirements
Any incidents, such as incorrectly declared goods and/or shipments or unsafe stowage or incorrect segregation identified by anyone in the supply chain should be notified to the Environmental Quality Branch of the MCA. Such incidents may be pursued under the Merchant Shipping (Dangerous Goods and Marine Pollutants) Regulations 1997 as amended.

Vessels and others in the supply chain are required to comply with the requirements of the Merchant Shipping (Reporting Requirements for Ships

Carrying Dangerous or Polluting Goods) Regulations 1995, as amended and the Merchant Shipping (Vessel Traffic Monitoring and Reporting Requirements) Regulations 2004 as amended.

11.   Advice
Specific advice on the carriage of dangerous goods by sea can be obtained from the address at the end of this section.

Annex 1 gives information where advice on the use of the IMDG Code and amendments to the Code can be obtained together with details of the other modal Competent Authorities involved in the transport of dangerous goods.

More Information
Environmental Quality Branch
Maritime and Coastguard Agency
Bay 2/03
Spring Place
105 Commercial Road
Southampton
SO15 1EG

Tel:	+44 (0) 23 8032 9100
Fax:	+44 (0) 23 8032 9204
e-mail:	dangerous.goods@mcga.gov.uk
General Inquiries:	24 Hour Infoline
	Infoline@mcga.gov.uk
	08706006505
MCA Website Address:	www.mcga.gov.uk
File Ref:	MS116/032/0017
Published:	May 2007

GB06/68827.00

An executive agency of the Department for
Transport

© Crown Copyright 2007

Safer Lives, Safer Ships, Cleaner Seas

ANNEX 1 - Consultation process, changes to IMDG Code and information sources

The MCA Standing Advisory Committee on the Carriage of Dangerous Goods on Ships (SAC) is a long established committee and consists predominately of Government and Trade Association representatives. The purpose of the SAC is set out in the terms of reference given below:

"To consider and advise on dangerous goods problems from the technical and shipping aspects, including precautions required to prevent or limit harmful effects to the environment which may result from incidents at sea."

It is important to distinguish between the function mentioned above and the separate process of consultation.

Consultation is governed by Government guidelines and is a formal process with open access. The IMO sub-committee on Dangerous Goods, Solid Cargoes and Containers (DSC) is where changes to the IMDG Code are discussed and agreed. The DSC briefing meetings are part of the consultation process together with the circulation of documents such as the draft to this MGN to Trade Associations and other persons who have expressed an interest but are not members of Trade Associations. The list of consultees has been developed over a period of years but if you wish to be included in the consultation process, please send your details to the address given previously.

Sources of Information

The MCA Dangerous Goods web-site (which has an introduction to the IMDG Code) will be the primary means by which any amendments to the IMDG Code and issues concerning the transport of dangerous goods by sea are notified to those to whom this Guidance Note is addressed. Alternatively, the point of contact is the Environmental Quality Branch of the MCA at the address given previously.

Information on IMO Publications can be obtained from the
International Maritime Organization
4, Albert Embankment
LONDON SE1 7SR
Tel: 0207 7735 7611
http://www.imo.org

The Merchant Shipping Regulations are available via the Office of Public Sector Information web site - http://www.opsi.gov.uk/

Current Merchant Shipping Notices (MSNs) and Marine Guidance Notes (MGNs) relevant to shippers and the carriage of dangerous goods in packaged form can be downloaded from the MCA web site http://www.mcga.gov.uk/ c4mca-guidance-regulation/mnotices.htm

Other relevant publications:

Further advice on this subject which is primarily for the information of surveyors will be contained in "The Carriage of Cargoes -Volume 1 - The Carriage of Packaged Cargoes and Cargo Units - Instructions for the Guidance of Surveyors.

Code of Practice on the Stowage and
Securing of Vehicles on Ro/Ro Ships"
(HMSO ISBN 0-11-552493-2) published
by the Office of Public Sector Information.

DfT Code of Practice Safety of Loads
on Vehicles found at http://www.dft.
gov.uk/stellent/groups/dft roads/
documents/page/dft roads 506864.pdf

Information on Dangerous Goods by
Road/Rail –
Department for Transport
Dangerous Goods Unit
Zone 2/34 Great Minster House
76 Marsham Street
London SW1P 4DR
Tel: 020 7944 2755
Fax: 020 7944 2039
E-mail: dangerousgoods@dft.gsi.gov.uk

Information on Dangerous Goods by Air –
Dangerous Goods Office
Civil Aviation Authority
Safety Regulation Group
1W, Aviation House
London Gatwick Airport South
West Sussex, RH6 0YR

Telephone: 01293 573800
Fax: 01293 573991
e-mail: dgo@srg.caa.co.uk

ANNEX 2 – General advice and carriage approvals

General Guidance

Documents of Compliance

Cargo ships of 500 GT and over and passenger ships constructed since 1 September 1984, and cargo ships of under 500 GT constructed since 1 February 1992, are required to carry a Document of Compliance if engaged in the carriage of dangerous goods on international and domestic voyages. Owners of vessels built before these dates carrying dangerous goods are encouraged to obtain such a document. More recently the format of that Document has been amended to show the spaces which have been categorised for the stowage of dangerous goods and its validity is limited to five years.

Safety Precautions and Bilge Pumping Arrangements

For ships constructed before 1st September 1984 to which the special requirements for ships carrying dangerous goods, contained in the Merchant Shipping (Fire Protection) Regulations 1998 do NOT apply, it is recommended that the bilge pumping system should be designed to prevent inadvertent pumping of flammable liquids having a flashpoint below 23℃ (closed cup) or toxic liquids, through machinery space piping or pumps. Where large quantities of these goods are carried, consideration should be given to the provision of additional means of draining the cargo space containing the goods.

The MCA will accept blanking off of the bilge suctions leading to the machinery space pumps. When 150 tonnes or more of toxic cargo or of flammable cargo having a flashpoint below 23° C (closed cup) is carried, alternative means of draining the compartment should be provided; e.g. by an ejector system or a suitable pump, certified safe for flammable atmospheres, located in the hold space.

Viscous liquids classified in accordance with 2.3.2 of the IMDG Code and assigned packing group III but with a flash point of less than 23°C should be stowed in accordance with the vessels Document of Compliance with regards to its flashpoint.

Cargo-passenger ferry voyages engaged on domestic voyages

Due to variations in local operating conditions and ship construction, cargo-passenger ferries operating within the United Kingdom or between the mainland of Britain and outlying islands may be permitted specified alternatives to the conditions of the IMDG Code with the agreement of the MCA. Shippers should contact local ferry operators for details of the service and any local conditions that may apply.

Offshore Supply Vessels

For the purposes of this notice, Offshore Supply/Support Vessels (OSVs) are those vessels which are engaged in the transport of stores, materials and equipment to and from mobile offshore drilling rigs, fixed and floating platforms and other similar offshore installations on voyages within the United Kingdom continental shelf.

By organizing the loading schedules for these vessels, the shipper assumes a high degree of control and responsibility for the cargo operation. All persons must ensure that correct segregation is at all times achievable and that the master is advised at the earliest opportunity of the quantity and nature of dangerous goods prior to loading at the quayside or backloading at the installation by being in receipt of the dangerous goods note.

Unless carried under the requirements of MARPOL Annexes I and II, the IBC or IGC Codes, or a procedure, based on a risk assessment of the operation and cargo carried and accepted by the Administration with regard to sea-fastening arrangements and discharge/loading equipment, the contents of portable tanks should not be loaded or discharged while the tank remains on board.

The guidance contained in MGN 282 as amended should be followed.

Containment Systems (Packages, Large Packagings, Intermediate Bulk Containers (IBCs) and Portable Tanks)

It is the responsibility of the consignor to determine the suitability of the containment system selected for the whole period of the proposed transport journey taking into account chemical compatibility between the contents and the containment system. Consideration should also be given to the temperatures within the CTU and any additional forces which it may be reasonable to expect during the journey.

Segregation

The "classes" for the purposes of applying the segregation requirements are those named in the table given in 7.2.1.16 of the IMDG Code. Note, there is also the need to consider the subsidiary risk when applying the segregation requirements. However for substances, materials or articles having more than two hazards (2 or more subsidiary risk labels) the segregation requirements are given in the Dangerous Goods List. It will not be possible to separately identify subsidiary risks from the labels/placards, only by reference to the Dangerous Goods List.

It must be noted that in addition to the requirements to segregate by class there may be a requirement to segregate by chemical properties and although column 16 of the Dangerous Goods List prescribes such categories of segregation e.g. "away from acids" it remains the responsibility of the consignor to ensure such provisions of the Code are met.

Paragraph 7.2.2.3 of the IMDG Code allows dangerous goods, which should be segregated "away from" each other, to be transported in the same cargo transport unit with the approval of the MCA, see below.

Requests for Approvals, certificates etc permitted under Chapters 1 to 7.8 of the Code

Requests for approval must be received early to avoid unnecessary delay and the approval must be issued prior to the goods being offered for shipment and loading of the cargo transport unit.

Such requests should be made by completion of an MCA Competent Authority Approval request form or by providing the information required on the form and, if appropriate, a Safety Data Sheet for the substance, certificates and drawings. The request forms are available either by phone, fax or letter to the MCA at the address given or electronically via the Dangerous Goods web-site.

For segregation approvals under paragraph 7.2.2.3 of the IMDG Code, details of the contents of the CTU and a diagram of how the goods are to be packed within the CTU must be submitted.

The type and nature of the information requested will vary depending on the nature of the request and granting of such an approval will be considered on a case by case basis.

The MCA may check/verify to ensure that the consignor has carried out correct classification procedures and ensured that the packaging is suitable for the goods that are to be contained within it. However, the consignor is responsible for defining correct safety procedures to ensure compliance with the Regulations.

All other IMDG Code requirements not subject to the approval must be complied with. The MCA may attach additional conditions to such approvals as are deemed appropriate for the maintenance and safety standards onboard ships.

A copy of an approval should accompany the shipment, or, where it is part of general legislation, there should be some reference to where the approval can be found and under which authority it is issued. Approvals are normally valid for transport to the port of destination.

Certain dangerous goods in IBCs must be carried in closed cargo transport units or in freight containers/vehicles, which should have rigid sides or fences at least to the height of the IBC. The MCA will consider alternative arrangements to the fencing provision provided a safety case is submitted to demonstrate an equivalent level of safety.

Annex 3 - Gases (Class 2)

Introduction

The IMDG Code contains general recommendations for the carriage of substances of this class and the following paragraphs are intended as amplification and indications of acceptable standards in respect of:

.1   pressure receptacles (cylinders);

.2   filling requirements;

.3   reference temperatures.

Receptacles

The MCA accepts:

.1   Pressure receptacles (cylinder) (as defined in the IMDG Code) of carbon steel, special steel or aluminium alloys designed, manufactured, tested and maintained in accordance with ADR (European Agreement concerning International Carriage of Dangerous Goods by Road);

.2   Pressure receptacles (cylinder) (as defined in the IMDG Code) made to the superseded standards BS 399; 400; 401; 1045; 1287; 1288; BS 5045 and HO "S", and aluminium pressure receptacles (cylinders) made to HOAL 4 and maintained in accordance with the appropriate parts of ADR;

Details of special receptacles of steel, copper, copper alloy, aluminium, aluminium alloy and pressure receptacles (cylinder) to standards other than those referred to above should be submitted to the MCA for consideration.

When aluminium alloy pressure receptacles (cylinders) are offered for shipment they should be suitably overpacked or carried in such a way that they are not affected by contact with dissimilar metals to avoid incendive thermite sparking.

Non European Union pressure receptacles (cylinders) offered abroad for shipment may be accepted provided they comply with the requirements of the national maritime administration of the country in which they are offered. Non European Union approved pressure receptacles (cylinder) filled in the UK may be accepted for export to a country where approval is recognised and for use onboard ships.

Shippers are advised that the use of foreign pressure receptacles (cylinder) imported into the United Kingdom containing substances of class 2 are subject to restrictions under domestic legislation.

Filling Requirements

The IMDG Code gives filling requirements in Chapter 4.1, P200 and P 203 for pressure receptacles (cylinders) and filling limits are specified in Chapter 4.2 for portable tanks.

Reference Temperatures

Pressure receptacles, which are to be used in the United Kingdom coastal climatic area, which is defined as the United Kingdom and the Irish Republic coastal waters, Irish Sea, North Channel and St Georges Channel, may be filled in accordance with the United Kingdom domestic requirements.

Battery vehicles

Battery Vehicles are vehicles containing elements which are linked to each other by a manifold and permanently fixed to a transport unit. The following elements are considered to be elements of a battery-vehicle: cylinders, tubes, bundles of cylinders (also known as frames), destined for the carriage of gases of Class 2 (with a capacity of more than 450 litres) and which are certified, filled, maintained in accordance with ADR and which have tie down attachments in accordance with the IMDG Code are accepted for short International journeys with or without tractor unit attached.

Pressure receptacles (gas cylinders) carried on Ro Ro Ships

(i)   The MCA has replaced MGN 19 by MGN 341. With reference to the Carriage of Gas Cylinders in boats, caravans and other vehicles where the gas is used solely in connection with its operation or business; information previously found in section 8 of MGN 19 has been further developed and the carriage requirements expanded. These requirements can be found below:

(ii)   This is a general approval and as such does not guarantee carriage in every case. It is important users inform the shipping line at the time of booking and not just prior to boarding, as operational constraints may limit the cargo including caravans being carried.

(iii)   In paragraphs 1 – 5 below inclusive, the gas supply should be shut off at the cylinders and all cylinders should be adequately secured against movement of the ship, away from sources of ignition and heat.

The requirement to declare to the shipping line prior to the sea journey remains.

Failure to declare may be considered an offence under the Merchant Shipping (Dangerous Goods and Marine Pollutant) Regulations.

The following gives detailed guidance on paragraphs (i) and (ii).

1)   *"Nominally empty"*

It should be noted that the IMDG Code considers empty pressure receptacles (cylinders) as dangerous goods unless purged and a certificate confirming this accompanies the cylinder.

2)   *Toxic gases*

Gases which are toxic are excluded from this general approval.

3)   *Oxygen/Acetylene*

The following provision applies to gases carried purely for maintenance work. One acetylene or propane/butane cylinder up to 35 kg gross mass and one oxygen cylinder up to 40kg gross mass, both pressure receptacles (cylinder) should be less than 1m in height and disconnected from any equipment prior to boarding the vessel. It should be noted that local regulations may not permit their carriage. No other class 2 or class 3 liquids are permitted in the same cargo transport unit (vehicle).

Note: It is advised that the local harbour authorities are contacted regarding their local regulations before taking acetylene into a harbour area.

4) **Propane and butane for private use**

Up to a total of 47 kg (excluding weight of gas receptacle)

5) **Calibration gases**

Gases which are not toxic and are used for calibration purposes may be carried provided the aggregate water capacity of the pressure receptacles (cylinder) or small receptacles containing gas (gas cartridges) does not exceed 50 litres.

6) **Ambulances**

Ambulances, which are, for the purposes of this notice, vehicles used to carry sick, injured or disabled persons to a place where they will receive treatment and then be returned, are in some instances unable to comply fully with the conditions of the Regulations. In recognition of the necessity for these vehicles to operate unhindered, the MCA accepts that they may be carried under the conditions as follows:

(i)   Gas cylinders carried must be for the sole purpose of the ambulance operation.

(ii)   The maximum number of cylinders carried must be six, of size 'F' or smaller (i.e. up to 60 litres aggregate water capacity), containing oxygen or UN 3156 Compressed gas, oxidising N.O.S (Oxygen, Nitrous oxide), (trade name entonox). Note size F has 9.4 litres water capacity.

Approximate dimensions of Size F Cylinder = 930 mm × 140 mm

(iii)   Cylinders should be declared to the ship's officer or shore side personnel prior to loading.

(iv)   All cylinders should be adequately secured inside the vehicle before loading against the movement of the ship.

(v)   Supply should be shut off at the cylinder except when necessary for the immediate needs of any patient carried within the ambulance.

(vi)   Leaking and inadequately secured or connected cylinders should be refused for shipment.

(vii)   The vehicle must be readily identifiable as an ambulance.

7) **Medical oxygen for personal use carried in vehicles not readily identifiable as ambulances**

Private vehicles used to carry sick or disabled persons may carry up to six, of size 'F' or smaller (i.e. up to 60 litres aggregate water capacity) containing UN 1072 oxygen, compressed provided the patient has a letter from a doctor stating they require medical oxygen.

In addition to the above conditions, shipping lines must be informed at the time of booking and use of oxygen on board ship is only in non smoking areas designated by the master.

Note: Shipping lines are invited to bring the above information to the attention of their customers.

Annex 4 - Waste

The transport of waste is covered by Chapter 7.8 of the IMDG Code, however, for the those involved with the carriage of wastes further guidance is given:-If waste is being shipped, it is the responsibility of the consignor to establish whether or not it is classified dangerous goods for sea transport.

If it is classified as dangerous goods for sea transport, it will be subject to all the provisions of the IMDG Code, as amended.

In addition, if the waste is classified as hazardous under the criteria of the Environment Agency (EA) for England and Wales, the Scottish Environment Protection Agency (SEPA), and the Environment and Heritage Service Northern Ireland (EHSNI) it will be subject to the written notification and procedures of Regulation (EEC) No 259/93, these bodies also regulate the transboundary movement of waste in the United Kingdom.

Wastes which are not classified as dangerous goods for sea transport according to the criteria given in the IMDG Code may present health risks to crew and passengers etc. Shippers of this type of waste, e.g. offal, some types of asbestos, hides etc, have to consider their duties and responsibilities under the Merchant Shipping (Carriage of Cargoes) Regulations, 1999 and the Merchant Shipping and Fishing Vessels (Health and Safety at Work) Regulations, 1997.

In addition, control over the transboundary movement of wastes outside the UK is exercised by competent authorities in each state who may not be the same as those bodies who regulate its transport.

It should be noted that sheeted bulk containers are not permitted under the IMDG Code.

Guidance for loading Cargo Transport Units (CTUs, Freight Containers) being used to carry waste (especially scrap materials)

The following is intended as guidance for those involved in the transport of scrap materials by sea. It should be noted that shipping lines may have specific additional requirements for loading scrap into containers.

1. CTUs must not contain dangerous goods unless they are correctly declared as such.
examples of dangerous goods:

- Closed (pressurised) containers e.g. aerosols, pressure receptacles (gas cylinder)
- Aluminium dross
- Magnesium
- Batteries (lead-acid, lithium etc)

2. Care must be taken to ensure CTU which are said to hold a single type of metal waste must not be allowed to be contaminated by other metals which may cause, or have the potentia to cause, a hazardous atmosphere to form.

3. Ensure that the contents of CTUs are free from acid, alkalis or other

substances liable to react with cargo to form a hazardous atmosphere.

4.   It should be noted that any CTU consigned for sea transport should be packed and secured to ensure even distribution of weight across the CTU in order to prevent movement of material contained.

Class 6.2 Infectious Substances

A detailed guidance document on the transport of infectious substances has been produced by DfT, CAA and MCA and is available at http://www.dft.gov.uk/ stellent/groups/dft freight/documents/ page/dft freight 504703.hcsp

For domestic voyages of Class 6.2 substances, UN2900 Infectious substance, affecting animals only; UN2814 Infectious substance, affecting humans and UN3291, Clinical waste, unspecified, N.O.S. or (Bio) Medical waste, N.O.S., or Regulated medical waste, N.O.S., class 6.2, where no other service exists other than on board passenger ferries, stowage category E is approved, away from living quarters and preferably under deck. All other conditions of the IMDG Code must apply to such goods, including the correct labelling of the goods and placarding of cargo transport units.

When transporting Clinical Waste under the above UN numbers, the vehicle is to be accompanied by the driver of the vehicle. Unless the Competent Authority have given approval to allow unaccompanied vehicles.

Animal by-products

It is the responsibility of the consignor to determine if the animal by-products meet the classification criteria of Class 6.2 and if so, transported in accordance with the IMDG Code.

During transport the integrity of the packaging, or leak-proof containers, should be maintained. The packaged material or containers must also be labeled to identify the category of the animal by-product being carried.

Detailed guidance on the Disposal of Animal By-products, including former Foodstuffs of Animal Origin, from Food Outlets, including its transport, is given in the Defra document of the same title available via http://www.defra.gov.uk/ animalh/by-prods/default.htm

It is also an offence under the Merchant Shipping and Fishing Vessels (Health and Safety at Work) Regulations to load onto a ship a cargo of animal by-products which is liable to leak onto the ships deck.

Annex 5 – Firearms and ammunition on Ro Ro ships

The following only applies to private firearms and ammunition for sporting use and is given as guidance to shipping lines.

It should be noted that firearms are not classified as dangerous goods only the ammunition and as such is subject to the requirements of the IMDG Code.

However, the following guidance is given:

Users are strongly recommended to pre-book advising the operator that you intend to carry ammunition in order to determine any local requirements.

All firearms should be accompanied by a current valid Firearm, Shotgun or Registered Firearms Dealer's (RFD) certificate and these should be available for inspection by either the booking in staff or port security personnel. Certificate holders should be aware of their requirements for ensuring the secure storage of arms and ammunition, for example: Any shooting equipment should not be visible when carried in vehicles.

The shipping line is advised to inform their local port security department to ensure smooth passage of the passenger and firearms/ammunition through the port area.

Ammunition

A maximum of 1000 cartridges of UN Class 1.4S per vehicle, which should be carried in the original manufacturers packaging, is permitted per vehicle without documentation. Quantities in excess of this must be declared and carried according to the full provisions of the IMDG Code.

Ship and Port Security Managers

Your attention is drawn to Transec Maritime Security Circular No. 2/02 The Carriage of Firearms and Ammunition

Annex 6 - Cargoes carried in cargo transport units which includes vehicles or on flat bed lorries

It is important to ensure that any cargo carried in a cargo transport unit is secured to prevent its movement during the sea journey where it may be subject to additional forces during the sea voyage.

Examples of cargoes which have resulted in incidents are:

(i)   Animal carcasses suspended from overhead racks inside the lorry have swung, resulting in the lorry breaking free despite being tied down.

(ii)   Steel carried on flat bed lorries or within vehicles must be secured to prevent its movement before being loaded onto the ship. If fabric strapping is used it must be protected from abrasion by corner guards.
The attention is drawn to port authorities and shipping lines regarding unaccompanied trailers where the securing equipment is owned by the delivering driver and may be removed when the trailer is dropped off.

(iii)   Drums loaded on to other drums without adequate separation protection and securing and the movement of these drums has caused the failure of the lower drum and hence resulting in a spillage.

Maritime and Coastguard Agency

Ro Ro Ships Vehicle Decks - Accidents to Personnel, Passenger Access and the Carriage of Motor Vehicles

Notice to all owners, managers, operators, masters, officers, ratings and shippers of vehicles, vehicle operators and passengers

This notice replaces MGN19

PLEASE NOTE:-

Where this document provides guidance on the law it should not be regarded as definitive. The way the law applies to any particular case can vary according to circumstances - for example, from vessel to vessel and you should consider seeking independent legal advice if you are unsure of your own legal position.

Summary

This guidance highlights the dangers to passengers and crew from moving vehicles during loading and unloading operations on boardRo Ro ships. It also contains the following interpretation of United Kingdom and international regulations:

(1) Specific guidance on issues relating to cargoes classified as dangerous according to the International Maritime Dangerous Goods (IMDG) Code that are being carried either for personal or business use by employees, passengers or contractors and that are not ships stores, is given in a separate MGN.

(2) Ships stores and equipment which are classified as dangerous according to the IMDG Code shall be stored according to either the Code of Safe Working Practice or the fire precautions for that space.

(3) Interpretation of SOLAS 1974, Chapter II-1 Regulation 20.3 given at paragraph 3, concerning access by passengers to the enclosed vehicle decks of Ro Ro ships, including permissible exceptions to that regulation; and

(4) Lists minimum safety conditions for fuel carried in the tanks of motor vehicles or alternative fuel systems.

This guidance is applicable to all United Kingdom ships and all ships within United Kingdom ports.

1. Introduction

1.1   A vehicle deck is a potentially dangerous environment due to congestion and movement of vehicles, many with flammable fuel in their tanks or dangerous goods being carried as cargoes. There have been accidents and at least one death of a crew member. The length of time passengers spend on a vehicle deck should be kept to a minimum and access by crew should be restricted to those who need to be there.

2. Statutory Requirements

2.1   Employers have a general duty to ensure, so far as is reasonably practicable, the health and safety of employees and other persons on board ship as required by the Merchant Shipping and Fishing Vessels (Health and Safety at Work) Regulations 1997, as amended.

2.2   The Merchant Shipping (Safe Movement on Board Ship) Regulations 1988, as amended, require that the employer and Master shall ensure that safe means of access is provided and maintained to any place on the ship to which a person may be expected to go. Additionally, the employer and Master are required to ensure that danger from the use or movement of vehicles and mobile lifting appliances is prevented so far as is reasonably practicable. Similar provisions are contained in The Docks Regulations 1988.

2.3   Employers (including consignors of cargo) are required by the Merchant Shipping and Fishing Vessels (Health and Safety at Work) Regulations 1997, as amended to be responsible for ensuring, so far as is reasonably practicable, safety and reduction of risk to health in connection with the use, handling, stowage and transport of articles and substances.

3. Passenger Access to Vehicle Decks

3.1   The SOLAS Convention Chapter II-1 Reg. 20-3, requires that "In all Ro Ro passenger ships, the master or the designated officer shall ensure that, without the expressed consent of the master or the designated officer, no passengers are allowed access to an enclosed Ro Ro deck when the ship is under way."

Except for access in emergency situations, consent should be limited to the following circumstances:

.1   In order to facilitate the ordered movement of passengers towards the end of a voyage and only if the master considers it to be safe, passengers may be allowed access to the vehicle deck provided the ship is not more than two ship's lengths from its berth;

.2   individual passengers under special circumstances and only for brief periods when they should be accompanied by a crew member;

.3   people with disabilities that seriously affect their mobility, where special arrangements have been made prior to the journey; and

.4   ferries on very short crossings where all vehicles are stowed on an open deck in accordance with provisions agreed between the ferry operator and the Maritime and Coastguard Agency (MCA).

4.   The Dangers of Accidents

4.1   The speed of cargo operations combined with large vehicles being manoeuvred in a restricted space is clearly hazardous to personnel.

4.2   There have been accidents where seafarers have been killed or injured during cargo operations involving flat-bed trailers or similar being driven by shore-personnel, despite the presence of signallers and ship's staff.

4.3   Many of the vehicles now being loaded on ships are larger than was envisaged when the ships were designed and built and are of such design that the view from the driving position, particularly when manoeuvering in reverse, is severely limited. This increases the hazards due to the limited walkway space available.

4.4   A number of cases of petrol spillage from vehicles carried on Ro Ro ferries have been reported. These cases and others involving the leakage of flammable liquids and gases could have given rise to serious incidents.

5.   Safety Provisions

5.1   The most effective method of ensuring the safety of personnel is to keep people and moving vehicles apart by preventing access to the decks during cargo operations. During normal operations this is impracticable but the fewer people that have access to the decks the less likelihood there is of accidents occurring. If access to these decks is necessary only the marked and authorised routes on decks and vehicle ramps should be used.

5.2   Personnel required to be on the vehicle decks as part of their job should be made aware of the dangers and the systems in operation for their safety, including the wearing of high-visibility clothing. Consideration should also be given to the need for the person in charge of cargo operations to communicate with drivers of vehicles and in particular the need to alert drivers quickly to any dangerous situation that may be developing.

5.3   Personnel involved in controlling vehicles should avoid standing directly between the vehicle being moved and any obstruction. The position chosen should minimize the risk of being trapped between the moving vehicle and an obstruction. Safety will also be enhanced by remaining in the driver's line of sight having regard to the driving position of vehicles in different countries. Personnel supervising vehicle deck operations are reminded that dangers are significantly increased when vehicles are driven on board at excessive speed.

5.4   Ship's staff should exercise special care where persons unaccustomed to vehicle deck operations require access to the deck. Car drivers and coach passengers are unlikely to be familiar with their surroundings or the operations involved, making them particularly vulnerable to the dangers.

5.5   Well illuminated, permanently marked and clearly signposted walkways should be provided for all those who require access to the vehicle decks both during cargo operations and when the ship is at sea. In addition, suitable barriers should be in place adjacent to doorways and exits that open directly onto the vehicle decks to prevent any person inadvertently walking straight onto the deck and into the path of a moving vehicle. Other measures such as deck mounted kerbs that force vehicles to maintain a safe distance from doorways and exits are also recommended.

5.6   Owners and operators are also strongly recommended to have suitable notices warning of the dangers at all locations where there is access to vehicle decks.

6.   Petrol and diesel in the tanks of motor vehicles

6.1   When vehicles are carried in cargo spaces which, under Merchant Shipping legislation or by equivalent arrangements agreed with the MCA, are suitable for the carriage of motor vehicles with fuel in their tanks for their own propulsion, it is important to ensure that on each vehicle:

.1   The tank is not so full as to create a possibility of spillage; and

.2   The ignition is switched off.

6.2   For diesel: the total capacity of the fixed tanks shall not exceed 1500 litres per transport unit (transport unit is a motor vehicle without an attached trailer, or a combination consisting of a motor

vehicle and an attached trailer) and the capacity of a tank fitted to a trailer shall not exceed 500 litres. A maximum of 60 litres per transport unit may be carried in a container specifically intended for the carriage of diesel. (This is also a requirement of the European Agreement concerning the international carriage of dangerous goods by Road (ADR) paragraph 1.1.3.3 as amended). Quantities of diesel carried in excess of this quantity shall be subject to the full provisions of the IMDG code.

6.3   Spare cans of fuel should not be carried in private vehicles.

6.4   Fuel contained in the tanks of vehicles, boats, or machinery such as a mobile generators or refrigeration units which are carried as a load can only be used for their propulsion, or their operation. These fuel tanks, subject to the quantity limitations given above, together with batteries present the same hazard as motor vehicles. The following requirements must also apply:

.1   The tank is not so full as to create a possibility of spillage.

.2   The ignition is switched of

.3   Any fuel cocks between the engine or equipment and the fuel tank shall be closed during carriage.

6.5   Generators which contain fue should be declared before loading These units are permitted to be carried subject to the conditions s out in paragraph 6.4 above.

7. Motor vehicles propelled by liquefied petroleum gas (LPG) or Natural gas, compressed or refrigerated (LNG).

7.1   Motor vehicles propelled by LPG should have gas storage and associated systems built to standards equivalent to the Road Vehicles (Construction and Use) Regulations 1986, as amended.

7.2   Motor vehicles propelled by liquefied petroleum gas (LPG) or liquefied natural gas (LNG), may be carried in the cargo spaces referred to in paragraph 6.1 provided:

.1   The ignition is switched off; and

.2   The gas is contained in a cylinder or cylinders with valves which should be closed when the vehicle is in position on board ship.

7.3   Only properly piped and fitted cylinders should be allowed. All cylinders of LPG or LNG should be properly secured.

8. Operational procedures

8.1   To guard against the possibility of incidents involving the spillage of fuel the following precautions should be observed:

.1   any vehicle showing visual signs of an overfilled tank should not be loaded;

.2   passengers should not be allowed access to vehicle decks once a vessel is underway, (see paragraph 3 above and when dangerous goods are carried the provisions of paragraph 7.4.5

Stowage of cargo transport units in Ro Ro spaces of the International Maritime Dangerous Goods Code);

.3   conspicuous "No Smoking" notices should be posted, together with notices warning against engines started before doors leading to ramps are opened and a crew member should be positioned to instruct passengers accordingly;

.4   a fire patrol should be maintained on vehicle decks during the passage unless a fixed fire detection system and a television surveillance system are provided;

.5   any spillage of petrol should be quickly cleaned up; sand boxes, drip trays and mopping up equipment should be provided for use on each vehicle deck;

.6a high standard of crew fire drill should be maintained;

.7   in the case of specially constructed ships where there are vehicle decks dedicated to the carriage of motor vehicles in a drive-on/drive-off condition, allowance should be made for the fact that flammable vapours and noxious fumes are evolved during the process of shipment. To ensure adequate air circulation, ventilation systems serving the vehicle decks should be in operation during any loaded voyage. When vehicles are being loaded or unloaded the number of air changes may need to be increased to ensure that any concentration of vapours or noxious fumes does not become a hazard to health[1].

9. Related Guidance

9.1 Further general guidance on the safety of personnel working on the vehicle decks of Ro Ro ferries is contained in Chapter 32 of the Code of Safe Working Practices for Merchant Seamen.

9.2 Further guidance is also in MGN 21(M) and the Roll-on/Roll-off Ships-Stowage and Securing of Vehicles Code of Practice (ISBN 0-11-552493-2).

More Information

Environmental Quality Branch
Maritime and Coastguard Agency
Bay 2/03
Spring Place
105 Commercial Road
Southampton
SO15 1EG

Tel:	+44 (0) 23 8032 9100
Fax:	+44 (0) 23 8032 9204
e-mail:	dangerous.goods@mcga.gov.uk

General Inquiries: 24 Hour Infoline
infoline@mcga.gov.uk
0870 600 6505

GB06/68827.00

MCA Website Address:	www.mcga.gov.uk
File Ref:	MS116/032/0016 I
Published:	May 2007'

Safer Lives, Safer Ships, Cleaner Seas

An executive agency of the Department for

Transport

---

[1] *The Control of Substances Hazardous to Health Regulations 2002 as amended (COSHH) apply to exhaust emissions and to the clearance of spillage in UK ports.*

INDEX

BIBLIOGRAPHY

International Safety Guide for Oil Tankers and Terminals (ISGOTT)

Liquefied Gas Handling Principles on Ships and in Terminals (SIGTTO)

Petroleum Tankship Cargo Handling Manual – Lorne & Maclean

Seamanship Techniques: Shipboard and Marine Operations, Third Edition – D. J. House. Published by 'Elsevier', 2004. ISBN: 0750663154

Cargo Work: For Maritime Operations – D. J. House. Published by 'Elsevier'. ISBN: 0750665556

Refrigeration at Sea; Munton & Stott

Marine Refrigeration Manual; Capt Alders

Code of Safe Working Practices (COSWP) – MCA www. containerhandbuch.de Shipboard Petroleum Surveys; a guide to good practice

Glasgow College of Nautical Studies (GCNS) - Cargo work notes

ICS Tanker Safety Guide (Chemicals)

The following HMSO publications:

SI 336 Carriage of Cargoes Regulation 1999
SI 2151 Additional Safety Measures for Bulk Carriers
Merchant Shipping (Hatches and Lifting Plant) Regulations 1988
Merchant Shipping (Load Lines) Regulations 1988
Merchant Shipping (Safe Loading and Unloading of Bulk Carriers) Regulations 2003
Ro Ro Vessels Stowage and Securing

The following IMO publications:

Inert Gas Systems
BC Code
BLU Code
CSS Code
IMDG Code
IGC Code
GC Code
EGC Code
IBC Code
BCH Code
International Grain Code
Code of Safe Practice for Ships Carrying Timber Deck Cargoes
International Convention on Load Lines
Guidelines for the Preparation of Cargo Securing Manual
STCW'95
SOLAS
MARPOL
Medical First Aid Guide (MFAG)
International Code for the Safe Carriage of Packaged Irradiated Nuclear Fuel (INF Code)
Specifications for the Design, Operation and Control of Crude Oil Washing Systems
Recommendations on the Safe Use of Pesticides at Sea

The following Marine Guidance Notices (MGNs):

MGN 284
MGN 60
MGN 36